Insect Masquerades

Insect

Masquerades

Hilda Simon
Illustrated by the author

FREDERICK MULLER

First published in Great Britain 1969 by
Frederick Muller Ltd., Fleet Street, London, E.C.4

Printed in Great Britain by
Fleming & Humphreys (Baylis) Ltd., Leicester & London
Bound by William Brendon & Sons Ltd.

SBN: 584 62025 X

To Professor Adolf Portmann

Acknowledgments

I gratefully acknowledge the information gained from the works of Harold Bastin, Alexander B. Klots, Adolf Portmann, F. E. Lutz, Edward C. Ross, and H. B. Kettlewell. I also especially wish to express my gratitude to John Pallister, of the Museum of Natural History in New York, for his generous help both in advising me on details and in supplying me with exotic specimens; and to John Clegg for his help with the last chapter.

Contents

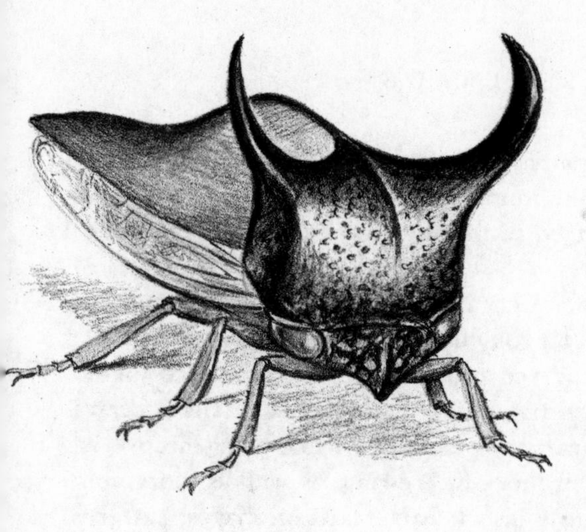

Introduction

OF ALL THE ANIMALS found on dry land, insects are not only the most abundant and widespread but also the most varied. The majority of adult insects are able to fly, but some are wingless. Many are so small that they can hardly be seen at all with the naked eye. Others may attain a length or wingspread of twelve inches or more. Some are dull-coloured and look like specks of dust. A great many others have beautiful bright colours and patterns.

Insect development, the growth from egg to adult, also varies a good deal among different groups. The most primitive insects, whose young are merely miniature editions of the adults, have what is known as *direct* development. The silverfish, a destructive household pest, is an example of a primitive insect. More advanced groups, such as grasshoppers, have a *gradual* development. Their young, called nymphs, acquire certain adult features as they periodically shed their skins and grow. In the most advanced insects, such as butterflies, moths, and beetles, there is a *complex* development, also called *metamorphosis*, from the Greek word for transform. Here the wormlike immature insect bears not the slightest resemblance to the winged adult, and has to pass through a pupal stage to attain maturity.

Due to this wealth of variety in size, shape, colouring, pattern, way of life, and habits, the roughly 700,000 species of insects that have thus far been discovered provide unlimited material for observation and study by naturalists and amateurs alike. Extraordinary facts about ordinary insects are constantly being discovered.

Matters are made even more interesting, as well as more complex, by the fact that many insects have taken on shapes, patterns, and colours that allow them to masquerade as something other than what they really are. There are, for example, insects that look like flowers or leaves. Others resemble thorns, twigs, lichens, tree bark—even bird droppings. And then there are those that imitate other insects, often so well that it takes an expert to tell the genuine thing from the fake.

Such masquerades are usually explained by biologists as the individual species' protection in the constant struggle for survival. This struggle is especially pronounced among insects because they are hunted for food by so many other animals—birds, reptiles, fish, and some mammals, as well as other insects. By masquerading as something they are not, many insects are often able to escape attack by predators. Such protection may be due to camouflage colours and patterns that allow the insect to blend in perfectly with its background, or to a display of "warning colours" that scare off would-be attackers. Some insects have a dual-purpose camouflage that conceals them from both their prospective victims and their enemies. The wearers of this camouflage are thus assured of a comparatively easy and carefree life.

Whenever an insect bears a striking resemblance to another insect of an entirely different species, the ''model'' usually is found to have very effective weapons that discourage attack by insect-eating animals. As we shall see later, the imitator, without having any real defence of its own, gets a definite advantage from looking like the genuinely protected kind. Which only tends to prove the validity, in the insect world at least, of the old saying that it is often what you appear to be, and not what you really are, that counts most.

The explanation of these disguises offered by scientists is both simple and logical. They say that the masks and costumes evolved gradually, over a very long period of time, and that only those insects with the most perfect disguises survived. Charles Darwin explained evolution of this sort as the result of natural selection, a weeding-out process that tends to eliminate organisms incapable of adjusting to their surroundings, while favouring those that are more adaptable. It thus leads to what Darwin called the survival of the fittest. The term ''survival of the fittest'' has often been misinterpreted as meaning that the fittest are the strongest or most aggressive. ''Fit'' in the Darwinian sense, however, simply means well suited for a particular way of life, and may apply to small, weak, and timid creatures.

As an example of what biologists call the ''survival value'' of a certain form, or variant, let us take an otherwise defenceless animal, such as a small bird. The familiar and well-loved shell parakeet, or budgerigar, is an excellent example. In captivity this bird may appear in several different, distinct colour variants—green, blue, yellow, and white. In the wild state, however, these birds spend most of their time among green foliage. It therefore seems only logical that the green individuals, which blend in with their background, will flourish, while the yellow, blue, and white individuals, being much more conspicuous, will be killed off more easily. This is probably the prime reason why many animal variants that can successfully be bred in captivity are never found in the wild state.

Why the different variants appear in the first place still remains unexplained. It would almost seem as though the creative forces active in nature throw a number of "sample products" on the market place of life, and then let its demands, pressures, and changes determine which one is to prevail. Animals are more or less helpless pawns in this game, for only man among all the animals has received the precious gift—and responsibility—of being able to influence and shape his environment according to his ideals, desires, and ambitions. All other animals are forced to adapt themselves to their environment if they are to survive. On the whole, they have not done badly for themselves, although quite a number of victims of environmental change have fallen by the wayside.

Darwin's theory of natural selection goes a long way towards explaining the evolution of a great number of interesting forms of life. It does, however, fail completely to explain others. Functional necessity and usefulness cannot by any means account for some of the unusual and wonderful shapes and forms occurring in our animal and plant life. On the contrary, we are frequently confronted with phenomena that defy all explanation, except, perhaps, the rather lame one of "evolution gone wild". But it is quite possible that these forms, which to us appear bizarre, grotesque, and without rhyme or reason, are part of an evolutionary pattern we do not yet understand.

In the pages that follow, we shall meet a number of insect masqueraders, freaks, and frauds. We must keep in mind, however, that insects are quite incapable of thought or reasoning in the human sense. Even though we may talk of an insect "masquerading" as something or somebody else, or "tricking" its prey, we must remember that no premeditated, reasoned action is involved. Insect behaviour is based, not on a choice of alternatives, but on instinct, a word designating a sort of "inherited knowledge", the origin and mechanism of which we do not yet understand. It is instinct that tells insects what to eat, where to lay their eggs, how to weave intricate cocoons, and indeed what to do in practically any situation. A few insects seem capable of acquiring a very limited amount of knowledge through experience during their lifetime. By and large, however, any act performed by an insect is due to instinct.

The interesting and unusual insects depicted and described in this book are only a very limited selection from a world-wide group. Some of them may be found in our own gardens or open spaces. Some inhabit the tropical jungles of South America, Asia, and Africa. Among them are insects that employ the most elaborate disguises in order to trick and trap their prey; others that use astonishingly clever camouflage to avoid discovery by their enemies; and still others that gain protection by imitating insects of different species. Finally, we shall be in the reviewing stand for a grotesque parade of insects that look like nothing else in the world except, perhaps, the figments of some science-fiction writer's imagination.

Even from the small selection offered in these pages, the reader should be able to get some idea of the seemingly limitless possibilities the creative force of life has at its disposal—of the fantastic diversity of shapes, forms, colours, and patterns that make our world the place it is: colourful, thought-provoking, and endlessly fascinating.

Traps and Trickery

SETTING TRAPS for unsuspecting victims is not a widespread practice in the insect world, for the majority of predacious insects get their food by actively hunting for it. A few, however, and especially a number of insect larvae, construct clever traps that deliver the food right to their mouths while they just sit there, usually more or less concealed, and wait patiently for the right victim to come along.

Perhaps the most familiar of these insect trap-builders are the peculiar creatures known as "doodlebugs". The name is used for the larvae of two unrelated kinds of insects belonging to different orders. They do not resemble each other when adult, or even in the immature stage. All they have in common is that they both lie in wait in burrows dug for the purpose of trapping their prey.

The best-known doodlebug is the larva of the ant lion, an insect which, in its adult form, looks very much like a small dragonfly. There are a number of different ant-lion species, but they all have similar habits. The larva, a heavy-bodied creature with long, slender jaws, digs a large cone-shaped pit in loose soil or sand. Concealed in the sand at the bottom of this pit with only its long jaws protruding, the doodlebug waits for small insects, especially ants—hence the name ant lion—to tumble into the pit, where it can grab them and suck them dry. The remains

The adult ant lion (upper left) and its larva, the familiar doodlebug, here shown ready to grab an ant that has tumbled into its cone-shaped pit.

The handsome six-spotted tiger beetle and its larva.

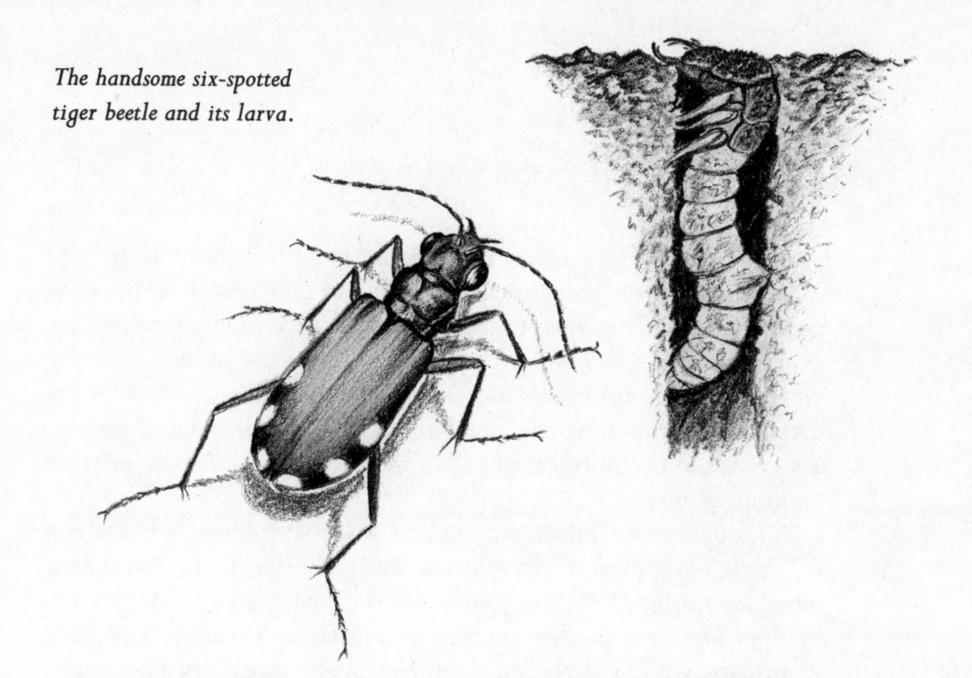

of the victim are then flipped out of the pit. Insects frequently try to climb out of the trap but are rarely successful, because the loose soil and steep walls of the pit make climbing difficult. In addition, the doodlebug hurls sand at the escaping victim to help bring it tumbling down to the bottom of the pit, within reach of those long, sharp jaws.

The other doodlebug, the tiger-beetle larva, has a slightly different method of catching its prey. This queer-looking creature digs a narrow cylindrical shaft, and plugs the entrance with its head. In this position the doodlebug waits, well concealed and motionless, until some unsuspecting insect wanders by. Then it shoots its head forward and grabs the luckless victim in its sharp jaws. The larva, which rarely leaves its burrow, has a pair of stout, hooked projections on its back. These hooks anchor the doodlebug firmly to the wall of the shaft and prevent its being dragged out by the struggles of some large victim.

Much better known than these rather primitive insect traps, and indeed the classic ensnarement, is the familiar spider web. Since ancient times it has been used, in the literature of many countries, as a symbol for any device by which a helpless or unsuspecting victim may be enmeshed and destroyed. Accordingly, spiders are often looked upon as the personification of malevolent cunning, a view based no more on fact than the proverbial but non-existent cunning of snakes.

Although often mistakenly called insects, spiders belong to a different class of animals, known as Arachnida, from the Greek word for spider. This group includes the scorpions and king crabs. Spiders are easy to distinguish from insects, because they have eight legs, while insects, no matter what the species or how much they may differ in other aspects, have only six legs.

In the case of both the spider's web and the doodlebug's pit, the trap consists of some device constructed by the predator to facilitate catching its prey. However, the insect world knows other kinds of "traps": predacious insects that do not bother to *make* a trap, because they themselves *are* the trap. Through an effective masquerade, such an insect manages to look like something innocent, harmless, or even inviting to its unfortunate victims, so that they will walk—or fly—straight into the arms of disaster without realizing what they have done until it is too late.

One insect that makes its living in this fashion is the queer-looking ambush bug. There are more than a hundred different kinds, most of which are found in tropical America and Asia. One commonly found in the Eastern United States is barely half an inch long. It is usually yellow or greenish-yellow, banded with black. This colouring, together with the bug's odd spiny armour, serves to camouflage it while it waits, frequently in golden rod or other

Concealed by body shape, colour, and pattern, this ambush bug lies in wait for insects in a golden rod flower.

yellow flowers, for a nectar-seeking insect to come along. Despite its small size, the ambush bug is quite a formidable killer, whose forelegs are adapted to form powerful, toothed grasping organs. Although it kills mostly small prey, it occasionally catches insects much larger than itself, including such dangerous and well-armed creatures as wasps.

A much larger and more varied group of insect predators are the members of the mantis family. Almost every region of the world has its own species of mantis. Typically, the most striking-looking as well as the largest kinds are found in the tropics.

Mantids have been well known since ancient times. Because of their "praying" attitude—head and anterior portion of the body held high, forelegs folded and raised, as in supplication—these insects have been regarded with superstitious awe, and even fear, by many peoples. The word *mantis*, which gives the family its name, means soothsayer in Greek. In German, the popular name

The large Oriental mantis is today found in many parts of the United States. Newly hatched young (below) are fully equipped for catching small prey.

of the insect is *Gottesanbeterin,* meaning god worshipper. In England and the United States, the common name is praying mantis, although the insect has many other local names, such as devil's coachhorse, rearhorse, and mule killer. Moslems insist that the mantis always prays in the fashion prescribed by the Islamic religion—facing towards the Holy City of Mecca.

This prayerful attitude, however, is most misleading. "Pious frauds", one naturalist has called the mantids, for they are quite possibly the most voracious of all predacious insects. Their appetite is truly incredible. Even though they belong to a group which also includes the grasshoppers and crickets, they have departed from the usual plant-eating habits of their relatives to become insatiable beasts of prey.

A mantis is never fussy about its food as long as there is enough of it. With the sole exception of ants, which it seems to shun, the mantis will eat anything it can catch, including members of its own family. All mantids are cannibals and will just as readily make a meal of one of their own kind as of some other insect. If the male does not step lively—and he apparently rarely does—the female will eat him, likely as not, right after mating. This seems a rather unromantic approach to marriage, and as the noted biologist Dr. Alexander Klots has remarked, a harsh way of making the bridegroom pay for the wedding breakfast.

Shortly after hatching from the egg, a young mantis, tiny as it is, thinks nothing at all of dining on its brothers and sisters. The adult mantis is so greedy, as well as wasteful, that it will strike out at another victim while still busily stuffing itself with the remains of the last one, and it frequently drops a half-eaten insect to be free to grab a new one.

Superbly equipped for its predatory way of life, the mantis is not an active insect. It does not have to be. On the contrary, moving about a lot would be distinctly to its disadvantage. Well camouflaged by coloration as well as by body shape and pattern, the mantis seems to know that sitting quietly and waiting will yield by far the best results. The most a mantis will do is stalk its insect prey slowly and stealthily, much the way a cat stalks a mouse.

The forelegs of the mantis are greatly modified to form extremely powerful grasping instruments, which hold prey in a vicelike grip. So strong are they that large mantids reportedly have caught small vertebrates including birds, shrews, and snakes. The forelegs are never used for walking.

While lying in ambush, the mantis waits in its "praying" position, its powerful, cruelly spiked forelegs folded and raised. But let an insect come within striking distance, and the forelegs will move like lightning, the spiked tibia—the "shin" of an insect's leg—snapping back against the equally spiked femur—its "thigh" —to pin the luckless victim in a death grip.

Foreleg of a mantis

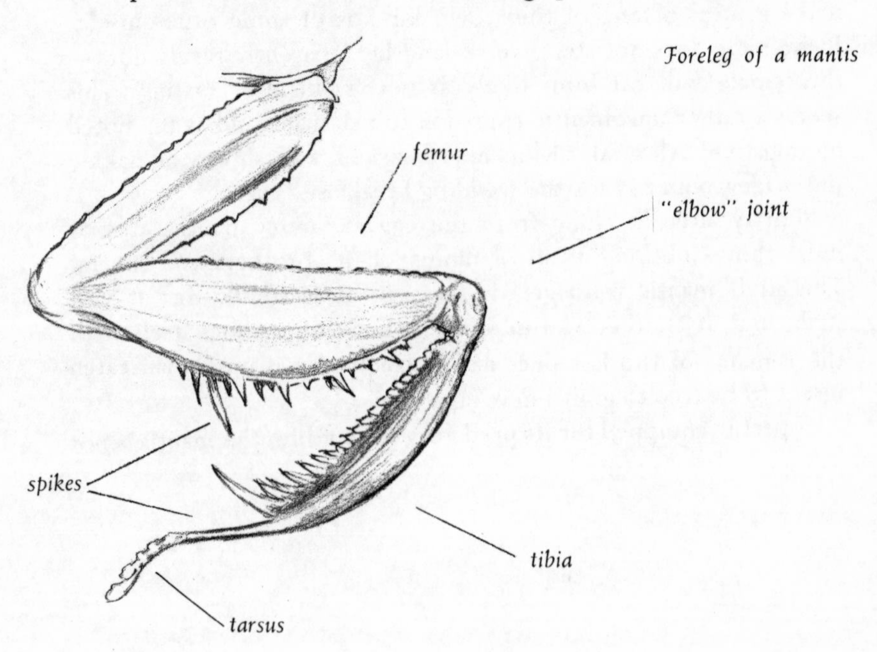

The Carolina mantis is the smallest of the species common in the United States.

All mantids have certain characteristics in common: an elongated body, a very long thorax, long thin legs, spiked forelegs adapted for grasping, and a head that can be turned about freely. It has been said that the mantis is the only insect that can look over its shoulder. Apart from these general characteristics, however, mantids may differ very much in appearance. Although the majority are coloured in brown or green hues, which blend into the foliage and branches of the plants where the insects lie in wait for their prey, mantids vary greatly in shape, hue, and pattern.

Four species are commonly found in the United States. One is native, one is European, and two are Oriental. All have predominantly brown or green coloration. The native Carolina mantis is the smallest of the four, measuring only about two and a half inches. The European and Oriental species, which are much larger, were introduced into the United States accidentally. Later, however, they were colonized deliberately by fruit growers and farmers, who were convinced that mantids ate enough injurious insects to function as a sort of natural pest control.

The bright green and white bands of this tropical mantis break up the body outline and help camouflage the insect.

There can be no doubt that mantids do destroy harmful insects in large numbers. Unfortunately, though, they do not distinguish between injurious and beneficial insects, and thus also destroy a great many of the most valuable fruit pollinators, such as honey-bees. Because of their indiscriminate slaughter of both beneficial and harmful insects, mantids are at best a mixed blessing. They cannot be compared to such unqualified "pest controls" as lacewing flies and most ladybirds. Both in the immature and adult stages, lacewings and ladybirds feed exclusively—and voraciously—on plant pests such as aphids, mealy bugs, scale insects, and white flies. They do not, however, destroy any beneficial insects at all, a good reason why they should be rigorously protected wherever they are found.

A single species of mantis may occasionally occur in two distinct colour forms. The European mantis, for example, has both a green and a brown form. Invariably, the green form frequents fresh foliage, while the brown individuals seek out trees and bushes with withered and decaying leaves. Both kinds thus have an excellent camouflage which works two ways: it conceals them from their prospective victims as well as from potential enemies.

In many other regions, and especially in the tropics, the imitation of objects in the environment has resulted in some strange and astonishing forms. There are mantids that have bodies flattened and shaped like leaves. Either green or withered leaves may serve as models. Some mantids are patterned and coloured to blend in with tree bark and lichens, and one even resembles bird droppings, apparently attracting filth-loving flies. Another kind looks so much like a stick insect—a harmless plant-eating member of the grasshopper family with a sticklike body and very long thin legs—that it takes an expert to tell the two apart. Because this mantis has been found in the company of true stick insects, naturalists assume that it preys upon them and is a kind of insect "wolf in sheep's clothing," unsuspected because of its appearance.

By far the most outstanding examples of fraud perpetrated by mantids are those afforded by the tropical species that simulate flowers. One of these is the famous rose-leaf mantis of India. This species has been known for several centuries, but its peculiar habits were never adequately described until the English naturalist Dr. J. Anderson supplied detailed information. In an article published by the Asiatic Society many years ago, Dr. Anderson draws a

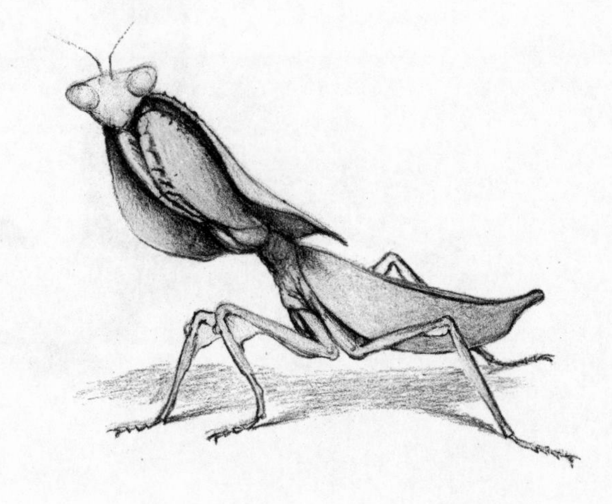

The flattened-out "hoods" over both thorax and abdomen of this tropical mantis have the shape and colouring of dead leaves.

vivid picture of the rose-leaf mantis as it lies in wait amidst the dense tropical foliage. Seen from above, he says, the mantis does not exhibit any very striking features, with the exception of the thorax and legs, which are shaped like leaves. The upper surface of the mantis is green, blending in with the surrounding foliage, and thus providing protection against discovery by birds and other insect-eating animals. The undersurface, however, presents an entirely different picture. "The leaflike expansion of the prothorax," says Dr. Anderson, "instead of being green, is a clear lavender-violet, with a faint pink bloom along the edges, so that this portion has the exact appearance of the corolla of a plant, a floral simulation which is perfected by the presence of a large, blackish-brown dot in the centre, over the prothorax, which mimics the opening of the tube of a corolla."

The Malaysian orchid mantis resembles a flower.

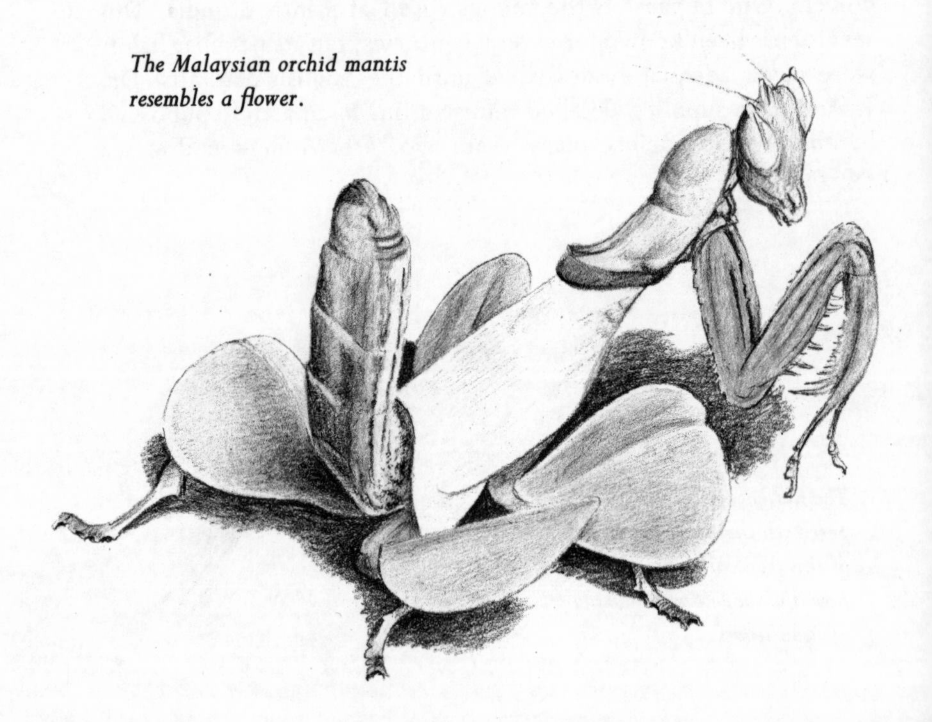

Anderson further observes that hanging head-downward in dense foliage is a favourite position of this mantis. Holding this position for long periods of time, it occasionally sways slightly, as if it were a blossom touched by a breeze. The forelegs, banded violet and black, are drawn up in front, thus perfecting the illusion of a flower. Attracted by this floral decoy, nectar-seeking insects are lured to their death.

Here, then, is a unique and sophisticated trap indeed: a portion of the predator's body, coloured and patterned in so exquisite an imitation of a flower that butterflies and other insects fly unhesitatingly to their doom. This goes far beyond the camouflage colours which help other mantids to avoid detection by their prospective victims.

In Mozambique, another species displays a similar flower-like pattern and colouring on the underside of its thorax. Even more striking, however, is the perfect imitation of a blossom achieved by the so-called orchid mantis found in the jungles of Malaysia. Not just one part of the insect but the shape and colouring of its entire body serve to create the illusion. This comparatively rare mantis was first mentioned by Alfred Russell Wallace, the English naturalist who was a contemporary of Darwin. Quite recently, Dr. Edward C. Ross, Curator of Entomology at the California Academy of Sciences, found an orchid mantis during a trip through the Malaysian jungles, and brought home some fine photographs of this amazing creature.

Usually the orchid mantis takes a position in the very centre of a cluster of blossoms formed by the so-called Straits rhododendron. Except for a small green band across the back, in the middle of the thorax, and some yellowish border areas, the entire insect is bright pink, in the various lighter and darker shades that match

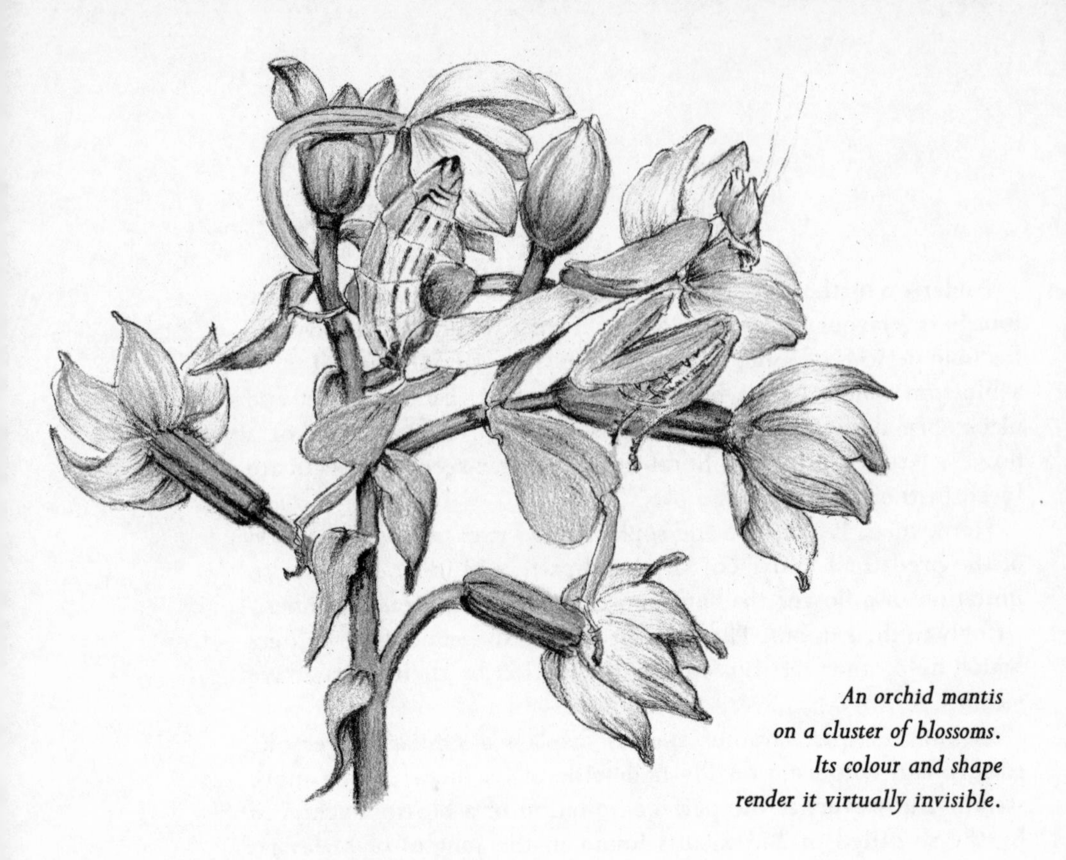

An orchid mantis on a cluster of blossoms. Its colour and shape render it virtually invisible.

exactly those of the blossoms it simulates. Even its eyes and antennae are light pink.

As the mantis rests quietly among the flowers, waiting for suitable prey—mostly butterflies—to come and pay a visit to the deadly "blossom", it raises its abdomen and bends it forward in an exact imitation of a floral hood. While its spiked forelegs are folded in the typical mantis fashion, the other four legs, parts of which are flattened in the shape of petals, are spread out symmetrically around the body. Even experts looking directly at this mantis have been unable to tell, as one naturalist expressed it, "exactly where the animal tissue commenced and where the flower ended." The imitation is so perfect that an orchid mantis sitting all by itself on a green leaf may easily be mistaken for a blossom.

There could hardly be a more striking example of a masquerade that turns an insect predator into the perfect—and perfectly baited—trap. The purpose of this masquerade is not to hide, but rather to be seen, and to be mistaken for something harmless, or even attractive and desirable. If birds and other enemies of the mantis are fooled at the same time, as of course they are, so much the better.

This double-purpose camouflage is, however, relatively rare in the insect world. By and large, concealing patterns and coloration are used by insects for protection only. In the following chapters are some fascinating examples of defenceless insects whose sole advantage in their struggle to escape attack by a host of hungry enemies lies either in looking like more formidable creatures than they actually are, or in making themselves all but invisible by melting into the background.

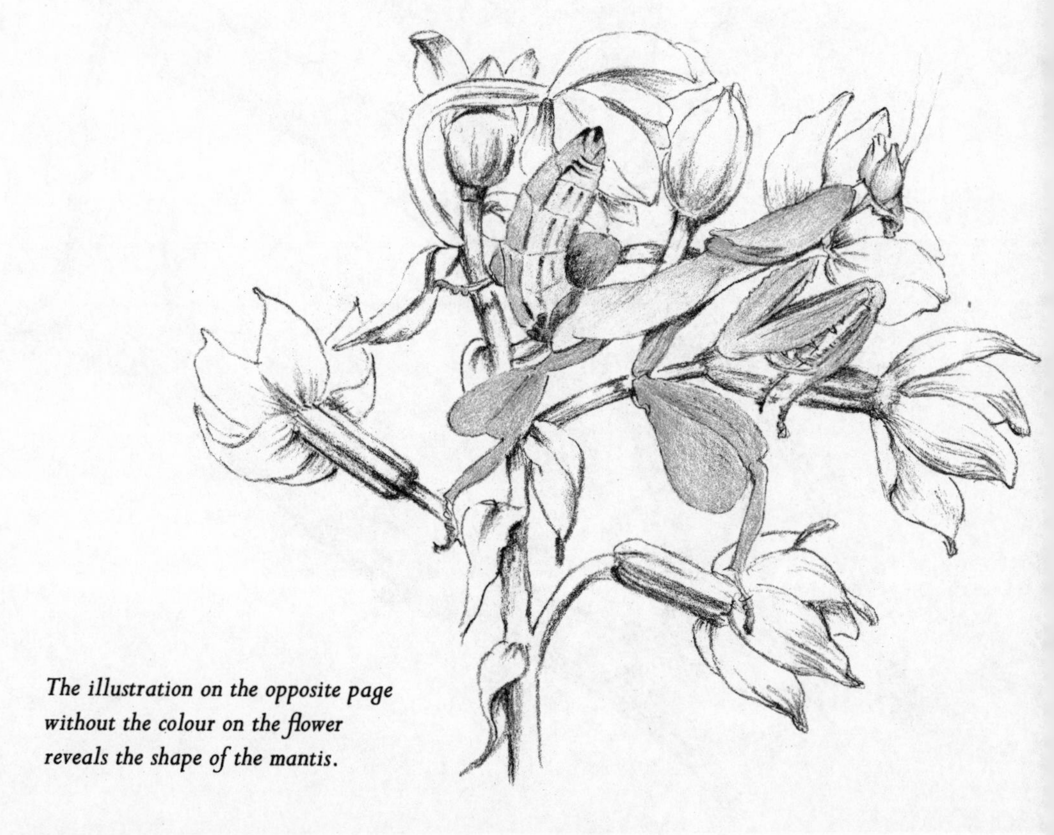

The illustration on the opposite page without the colour on the flower reveals the shape of the mantis.

Camouflage

DERIVED from the French word *camoufler,* which means "to disguise", *camouflage* has become an internationally accepted military term for protective disguise. In times of war, camouflage by such means as paint or screens is used to hide batteries, ships, camps, and arsenals from enemy eyes by causing them to blend in with their surroundings. Many animals for whom life is a constant struggle to avoid being eaten by other animals need camouflage colouring and patterns which will allow them to blend into the background for very much the same reason—in order to hide from enemies. Camouflage thus ranks as one of the prime means of survival in the animal world, every bit as important to some animals as speed, agility, or strength is to others. Ways and means of concealment are consequently as manifold and different as are the diverse sizes, shapes, colourings, and living habits found in the various members of the animal kingdom.

For insects, which furnish so large a part of the food consumed by other animals, all protective devices, including concealment, are of vital importance in the daily game of life and death. It is therefore hardly surprising to find some of the fanciest and most intricate camouflage "costumes" among members of the insect class. The perfection of disguise displayed by certain insects cannot be matched by animals of any other group.

Prerequisite for remaining undiscovered in the midst of inanimate or stationary objects is the ability to avoid eye-catching movements, and to stay still for long periods at a time. Scouts and infiltrators who have to get past enemy guards must learn how to remain motionless and melt into the background in order to escape discovery. The same applies to all camouflaged animals. After all, the mantis that fools everybody by looking so convincingly like a flower while sitting quietly in its place will fool

The Indian dead-leaf butterfly, colourful above, looks like a decayed leaf when it sits with wings closed (right).

nobody at all if it is caught walking away. This, of course, holds true for all insects that find protection by imitating inanimate objects, such as sticks and stones or bird droppings, or parts of plants—leaves, twigs, thorns, bark, lichens, and the like. As long as these insect masqueraders are motionless, they stand an excellent chance of escaping detection, and consequently, of not providing a meal for some hungry predator. For this reason, we find that insects depending on camouflage for protection are likely to stay in one position without moving for long periods at a time. Some move about only in the dark.

Among the most spectacular and widely known examples of perfection in camouflage are the dead-leaf butterflies, especially those of the Indo-Australian genus *Kallima*. Seeing only the brightly coloured upper wing surfaces, no one could guess what these butterflies look like in a resting position, which displays the undersides of their wings. Seasoned naturalists are on record as having searched unsuccessfully for this butterfly among the leaves of a bush on

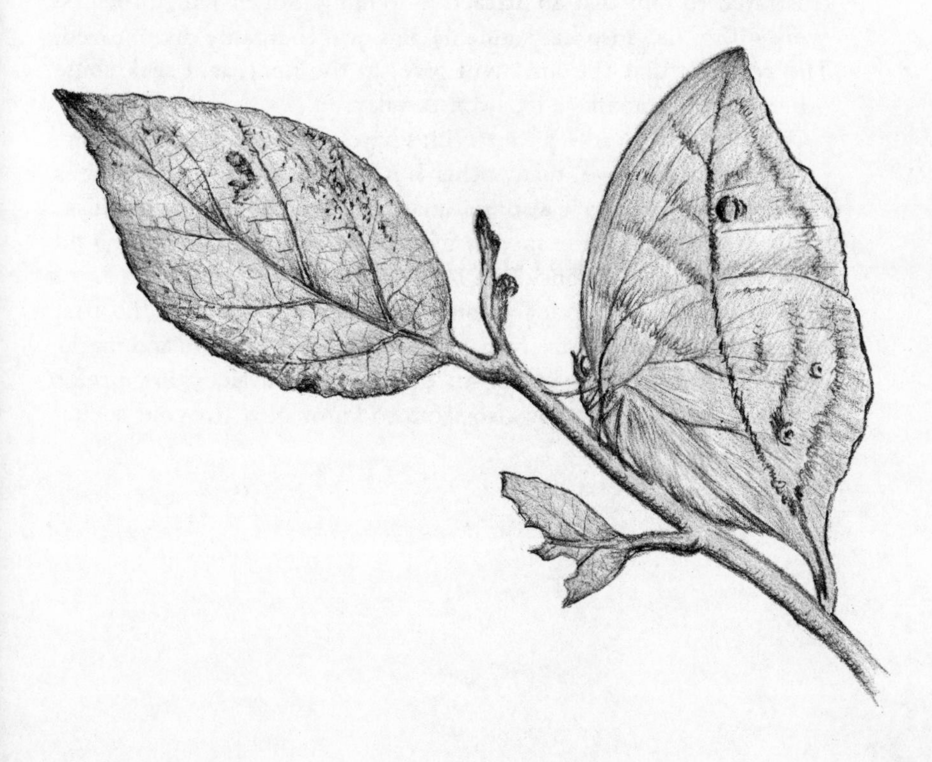

which they had seen it alight. Only the most careful inspection of the bush revealed the one dry leaf that was no leaf at all, but the missing insect.

The shape and colouring of the wings of these *Kallima* butterflies combine to create the perfect disguise. The front wings are pointed, and the hind wings have little slender tails. The undersides of the wings are light brown, with darker lines simulating a leaf's midrib and veins, and with small discolorations that look like decay spots. When the butterfly comes to rest on a twig, it claps its wings together so tightly over its back that they appear to be a single, leaf-shaped piece. Its head, legs, and body are all but hidden, and the tails of its hind wings just touch the twig. Thus the illusion of a dead, decaying leaf still adhering to the twig is complete.

The vanishing act of these butterflies is so sudden and so thorough that it mystifies even the human observer who knows what to expect. Small wonder that a hungry bird is confused and frustrated to find that an attractive-looking morsel which seemed well within its grasp has suddenly and unaccountably disappeared. The result is that the bird will give up the hunt, and seek some other prey. Camouflage has won the day.

Although the dead-leaf butterflies have attained an amazing perfection in camouflage, many other butterflies and moths—adult as well as immature—are also past masters in the fine art of disguise. Quite frequently, these insects manage to look like something no bird would possibly consider a likely meal.

Moths especially count among their number some of the best insect camouflage artists. Not only are the wing colours and markings of certain moths perfect matches for the surfaces they prefer as resting places, but they also seem to know how to avoid having their wings cast a tell-tale shadow that would make them more easily visible. When a moth whose wings have a bark-like pattern comes to rest on the trunk of a tree, it spreads its wings flat sideways, so that they cast practically no shadow at all, and appear to merge into the bark.

It seems most remarkable that these moths instinctively select the right kind of surface for their resting place. Rarely do they pick a background that differs much from their own wing colour and pattern, apparently not feeling comfortable on any except the "right" surface. As moths cannot see themselves, the question arises as to how they know exactly which *is* the right background. It has been suggested that they are guided by the colours of the hairs and scales around their eyes and at the base of their front wings, but much more research has to be done before we will know the answer for certain.

The colouring and design of its forewings let this moth blend in with the tree bark on which it is resting.

The green sphinx moth is difficult to detect among green foliage.

How effective as a protective device concealing patterns can be is illustrated by a story told by Dr. Ross, the naturalist whose photographs of the rare orchid mantis were mentioned in the preceding chapter. A collector of insects from all over the world, he frequently makes extensive trips for the purpose of adding to his collections. During one of his trips, he took a photograph of a flat-tailed gecko—a small lizard found in many warm countries—because he was intrigued by the gecko's effective camouflage. The reptile's mottled skin pattern was an excellent match for the bark of the tree it had chosen as its abode. Much later, after he had returned home, Dr. Ross studied the photograph carefully. It was only then that he discovered a detail which both he *and* the gecko had missed at the time: a small moth sitting right under the gecko's nose, its wing so exquisite an imitation of the tree bark that the insect had become truly invisible.

In England, naturalists have recorded an interesting case which shows how tremendously important cryptic, or concealing, coloration and pattern may be in determining which of several variants of a species will survive in a changing environment. The particular insect involved is a fairly common European species of moth, belonging to a very large world-wide group. Until about a hundred years ago, this moth, popularly called the peppered moth, was found all over the British Isles in its light-coloured form, showing dark scrawls and markings on a white background, and only occasionally in a blackish-brown variant. At that time, the dark, or melanic, specimens were much sought after by collectors, because they were exceedingly rare.

With the rapid industrial growth in many regions of the British Isles, tons of soot began to be poured into the atmosphere every day. Gradually, in these industrialized areas, the surfaces upon which the peppered moths habitually rested became steadily darker. Just as steadily, the "normal", pale-coloured variety of the moth

This cossid moth resembles a wilted blossom that has dropped from its stem.

gradually decreased in numbers, with a corresponding increase in the population of the dark form. In badly polluted areas, the melanic variant has by now practically replaced the light-coloured form. Careful and continuous observations revealed that the light-coloured moths, which liked to rest on lichen-covered trees and similar surfaces, became conspicuous as these surfaces darkened, making the moths easy prey to birds. Conversely, the dark individuals, which before had been conspicuous, now blended in with the dark background, thereby escaping discovery and attack. This gave the dark moths a chance to survive, reproduce, and multiply. Today only the rural areas of England still have large populations of the light-coloured form of the moth.

This case, which has been recorded in detail, is an excellent object lesson on how environmental changes and pressures may favour—although not create—one of several variants of a given species. It is therefore a perfect illustration of Darwin's theory of natural selection.

For many moths, tree bark is a favourite "model" Chances are that almost any kind of bark, whether it is dark or light, brown or grey, fine-grained or coarse, is matched by the wing colouring and design of some moth species. Lichens, those peculiar plants that grow on stones and tree bark, are also frequently imitated. One moth species, called the green marvel, is pale green with irregular dark blotches and scrawls on its wings. When this moth rests quietly on a patch of pale-green lichens, it becomes all but invisible. The broken-twig moth, on the other hand, has a shape and coloration that make it look very much like a small piece of decayed wood.

ꞏred moths, a light-coloured and a melanic variant,
n a soot-blackened tree trunk.

Left to right: the green marvel moth resting on pale-green lichens; with the colour removed from the background, the insect stands out clearly; on a solid-green background, the moth would be very conspicuous.

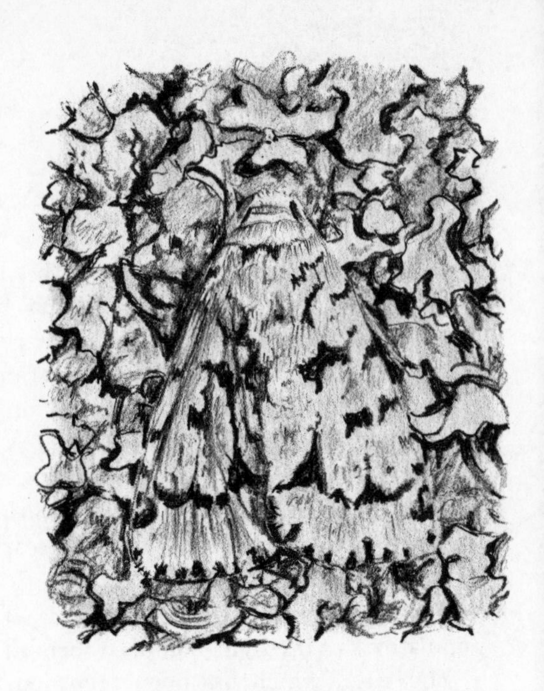

While many adult butterflies and moths are excellent imitators, there are also a considerable number of caterpillars that successfully mimic inanimate objects. Aided by a variety of different shapes, colours, and markings, caterpillars manage to imitate dead leaves, twigs, leaf stems, bird droppings, and other objects that hold no interest at all for birds or reptiles looking for a meal. Here, too, the ability to remain motionless is important, but caterpillars in general are not the most active of insects, since their activity is confined mainly to eating as much as they can.

Some of the best caterpillar disguise artists are found among the geometrids, a large moth family.(Moths are slightly more primitive cousins of the butterflies, and both groups belong to the huge order of the Lepidoptera, or scale-winged insects). The scientific name of the family, Geometridae, is derived from the Greek, and means, literally, earth measurers. Anybody who has ever watched one of these caterpillars will confirm that the scientific name is very descriptive, as are their popular names, looper and measuring

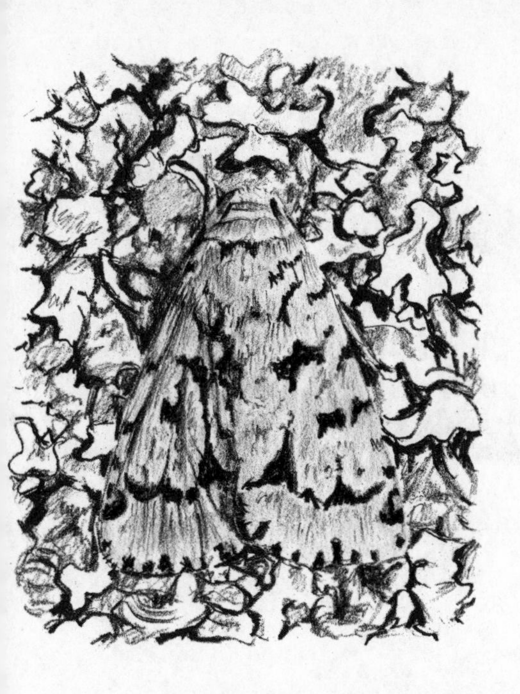

worm, even though they are not worms. These caterpillars move forward with a queer looping gait, which does indeed give the impression that they are measuring off every step they take. A pleasant superstition concerning measuring worms is that if you let one of these caterpillars crawl over you without molesting it, you will soon get a new suit of clothes.

A looper progresses by lifting the front end of its body up and forward, then bringing it down, taking hold with its front legs, and finally drawing its rear end forward, thereby forming a loop with the middle section of the body. This peculiar method of locomotion is due to a lack of many of the larval *prolegs,* the soft, fleshy, stubby legs which caterpillars have in addition to the six "true" legs that are the hallmark of all insects.

Many loopers are noted for their resemblance, in a resting position, to small twigs or leaf stems. Their long slender bodies frequently have irregularities of shape which greatly facilitate this disguise, further enhanced by the appropriate green or brown

Which part of this twig is an insect?
For the answer, see the opposite page.

coloration. To accomplish its imitation of a small twig, a caterpillar will grasp the stem on which it is perched with only the hindmost pair of prolegs, stretch its body stiffly into the air at an angle to the stem, and then remain motionless for considerable periods of time. How well these loopers can play their part was impressed on one collector who had cut off and taken home a

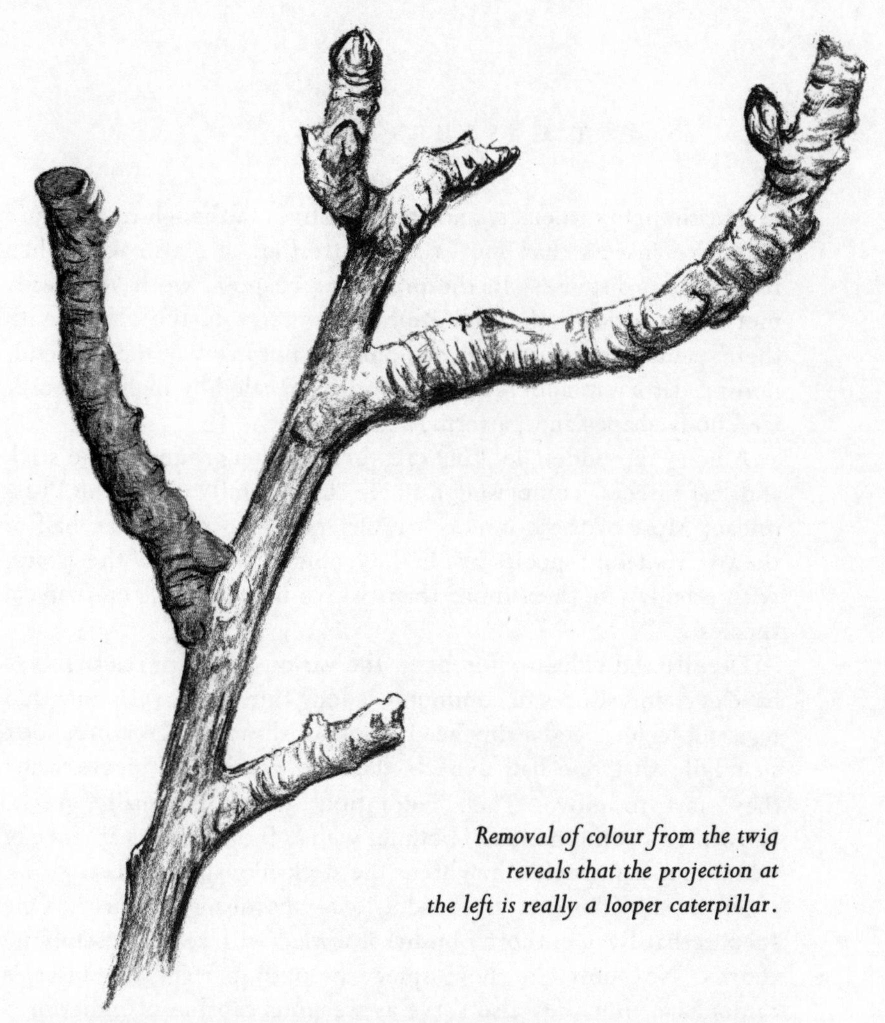

Removal of colour from the twig reveals that the projection at the left is really a looper caterpillar.

small branch because the cocoon of a moth adhered to one of the twigs. He was most surprised when he examined the branch at home and suddenly saw the shortest twig starting to walk, or rather loop, away! Throughout the commotion caused by the cutting and carrying of the branch, the caterpillar had stayed motionless in its "twig" position.

Grasshoppers, locusts, and their relatives, although much more primitive insects than moths and butterflies, are also tops when it comes to disguises. In the preceding chapter, we have already met the mantids—the bloodthirsty members of the clan—with their special kind of ambush camouflage. But many of the peaceful, non-predatory members are also well concealed by highly specialized body shapes and patterns.

Among the oddest-looking creatures of this group are the stick and leaf insects, comprising a single, large family called the Phasmidae. Most of these insects are Oriental, and more than half of the two thousand species live in the tropics. The giant of the group, with a body length of more than twelve inches, is also a tropical species.

Despite individual differences, the various kinds of stick insects have certain features in common—a long thin body, very long thin legs and feelers, and a tiny head. Some of these odd creatures look so fragile that one half expects them to break into pieces when they start to move. Their coloration, which is usually green, brown, or a combination of both, as well as the complete absence of wings in many species, heightens the stick-like appearance.

Some stick insects have additional disguising features. One species that lives in thorny bushes is armed with spines resembling thorns. Not only do these spines help to perfect the insect's camouflage, but they also serve as weapons capable of inflicting a nasty wound.

Stick insects would look like twigs in any position, but the resemblance is heightened by the peculiar poses they assume. They habitually rest with their forelegs stretched out straight and close together, making it difficult to tell exactly where the legs end and the body begins.

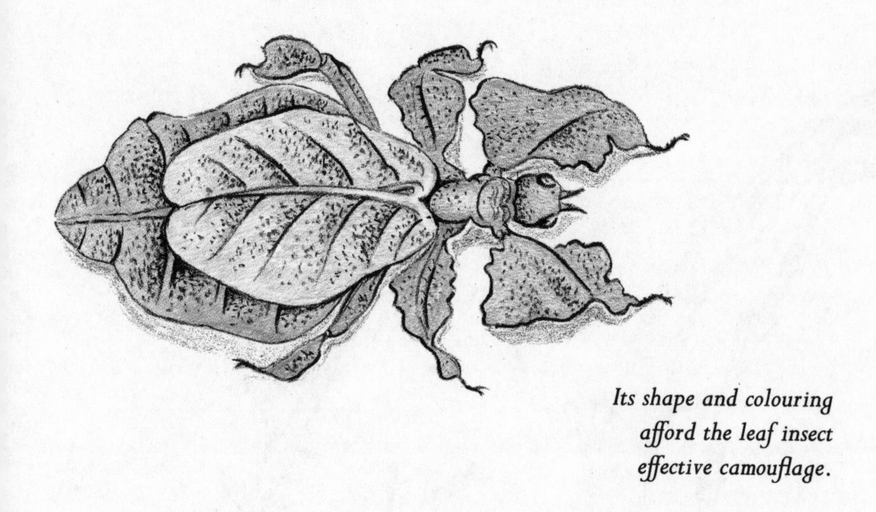

Its shape and colouring afford the leaf insect effective camouflage.

One of the common American stick insects—often called walking sticks—is partly brown, partly green. This species feeds on the leaves of oak, cherry, and locust trees, and, in great numbers, may cause defoliation. Generally, however, it is not considered a serious pest.

Despite their good camouflage, these "twigs on legs"—slow-moving, wingless, helpless creatures—are quite often caught by birds. Nevertheless, their disguise helps enough of them to escape detection to ensure the survival of the species.

Leaf insects, close cousins of the walking sticks, make use of a different part of the plant in their masquerade. As the name implies, they go through life looking as much like a leaf as possible. Whereas stick insects are long and thin, leaf insects are flat and broad. Body, wings, and legs are shaped, patterned, and coloured to resemble a leaf down to the last detail—midrib, veins, decay spots, and all.

The leaf insects are all tropical, and many of them are found on islands. Some of them are good-sized insects—females may measure up to four inches. As long as they rest quietly among the

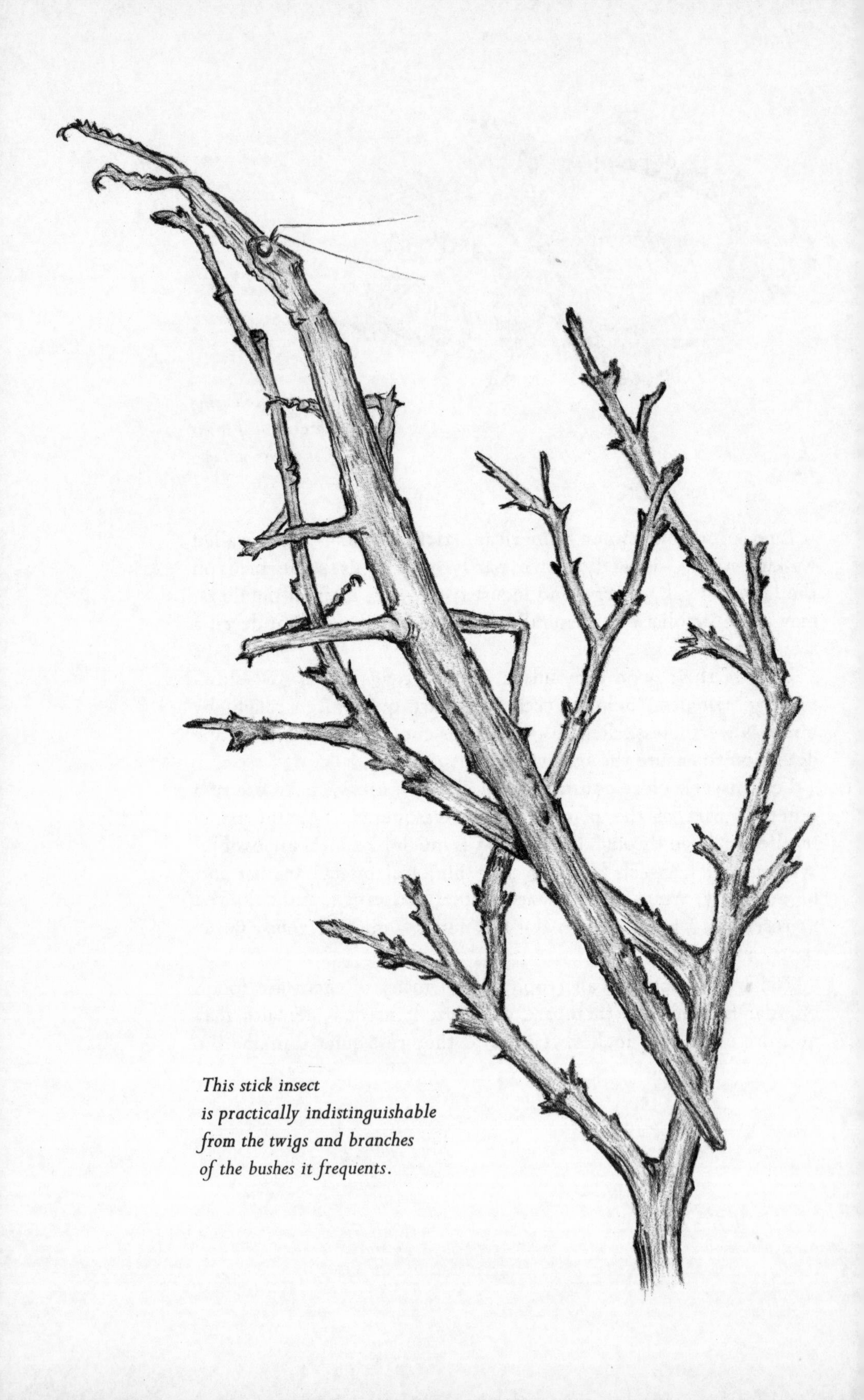

This stick insect
is practically indistinguishable
from the twigs and branches
of the bushes it frequents.

leaves of their plants, they are extremely difficult to detect. In order to reduce further the chances of being discovered, all the members of the phasmid family usually feed at night, so that they have no need to move about in the daytime. During the day they are totally inert—not asleep in the ordinary sense, for they can be handled, and even mutilated, without showing any signs of animation. This phenomenon has recently aroused new interest in the research of the Russian biologist Peter Schmidt, who experimented with stick insects in the early years of the twentieth century. According to his findings, certain insects are periodically in a state of trance produced by a chemical reaction to light. These insects come to life again only after sunset, when the daylight begins to fade.

From the variety and wealth of the camouflage patterns found in insects, as well as from specific examples such as the peppered moth, it is abundantly clear that many defenceless insects could not survive without the aid of these concealing disguises. No less important, however, to other insects without weapons of their own, is a different kind of masquerade, which aims, not at concealment, but rather at the opposite: exposure, recognition, and avoidance by insect-eating animals. In the next chapter, we shall meet some insects that do not bother to hide from their enemies, because they rely upon a bluff for safety and protection.

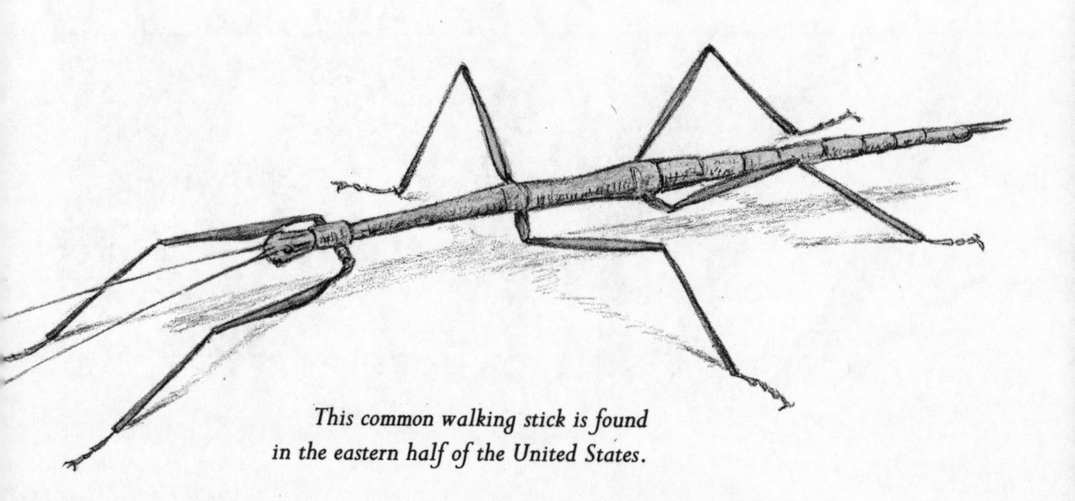

This common walking stick is found in the eastern half of the United States.

Warning Signals

On unhurried wings, the stately monarch butterfly of America sails through the air, stopping to sample a flower. Its broad wings gleam in a bold pattern of orange-brown, black, and white. Despite its conspicuous appearance, the monarch does not display the nervous, hasty, fluttering movements so typical of many other butterflies, nor does it show any desire to hide. On the contrary, the handsome fellow seems serenely unconcerned about being spotted by one of the many sharp-eyed birds engaged in their day-long search for food. This big butterfly's behaviour conveys the impression that, unlike most others of its kind, it feels no need for haste while flying about in plain sight of friend and foe alike.

A large black-and-yellow hornet alights on an overripe pear, and is soon joined by others. They busy themselves with the sweet juices that ooze from the bruised patches on the skin of the fruit, lapping them up eagerly. They feed without haste, and without any attempt at concealing themselves. Quite obviously, the hornets are not at all nervous about the possibility of an enemy attack.

Sitting at the very top of a tall ramrod-straight milkweed plant, and vigorously chewing on one of the tender, young green leaves, a milkweed beetle gleams in the sunlight. There could hardly be a more conspicuous sight than this boldly patterned insect with its contrasting colours of bright scarlet and black outlined against the green background. Yet the beetle stays out in the open, easily visible even at a distance, and apparently does not have to pay, for such boldness, the penalty of sudden and violent death.

In all the instances described above, and in a great many others found throughout the insect world, there is an excellent reason for this seemingly suicidal behaviour. It is not accidental; the insects somehow seem to know that they do not have to fear exposure as much as others of their kind. We must remember, of course, that knowledge in the human sense is not involved here.

Wasps enjoy the sweet juices of overripe fruit.

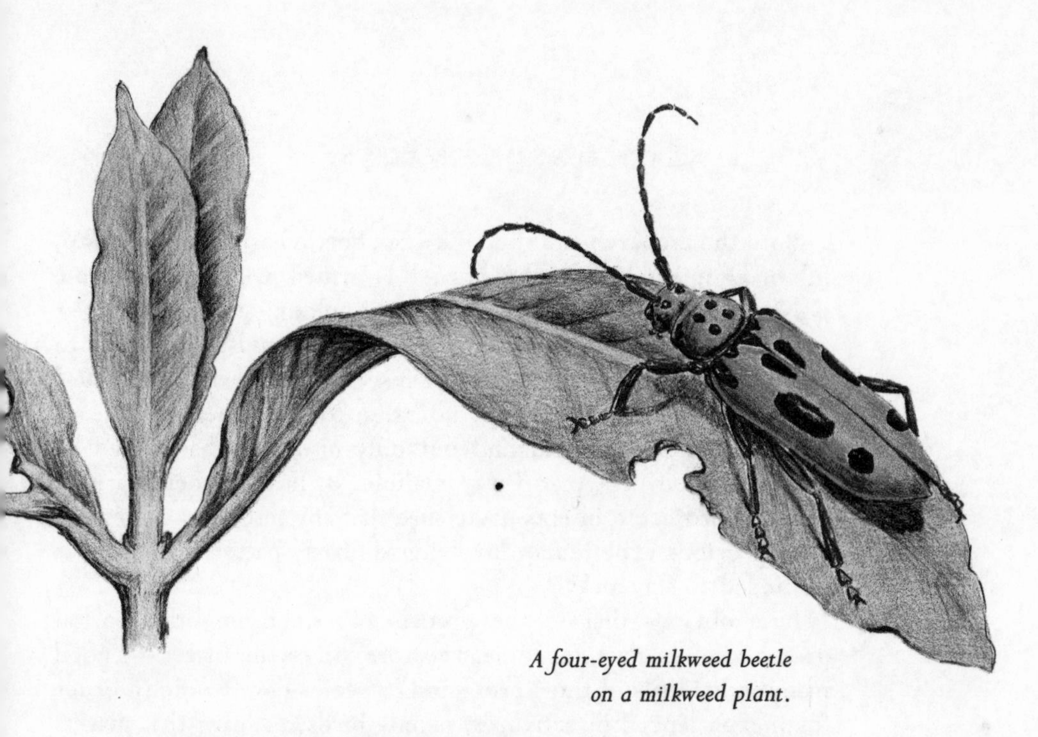

A four-eyed milkweed beetle on a milkweed plant.

Insects do not have the kind of brain found in higher animals. The insect brain is not only minute, but also very simple, and exerts very little control over the body. Ganglia, tissues containing nerve cells, serve as nerve centres for various parts of the insect's body. (See diagram of the insect's anatomy on page 90).

Instinct tells the monarch, the hornet, and the milkweed beetle that their best protection lies, not in trying to hide, but rather in showing their bright colours. Quite frequently, their behaviour appears so deliberate and calculated that if we were talking in human terms, we would say they *flaunt* their bold, colourful wing and body patterns. Why they do this becomes clear when we realize that what to us looks merely attractive and ornamental, is in reality a warning signal telling insect-eating animals to stay away. Evil-tasting! Dangerous! Obnoxious! Those are the messages flashed by the bright colours.

Both the monarch and the milkweed beetle have highly distasteful body juices, while the hornet is armed with a formidable poison sting. Bold, easily recognizable colour patterns advertise the fact that here is a protected insect. It is most important to get the message through *before* the insect is attacked, for the best defensive device would be of no value to its owner if birds or other predators were to find out only *after* they had killed or mutilated their prey that it was inedible. By flashing their warning colours, protected insects make sure that any insect-eating animal with previous experiences involving similarly patterned insects is reminded to stay away.

It is obvious that in the process of establishing this partial protection—partial, for some predators will eat *any* insect—a good many individuals of the "protected" species have to die in order for inexperienced insectivores, mainly birds, to learn that insects displaying certain colours and patterns should be shunned. This, of

The locust borer is a wasp-mimicking beetle.

This clearwing moth is also a good wasp mimic.

course, follows a pattern recognizable throughout nature: the survival of the species, not the individual, seems to be what matters.

Once relative immunity has been established for one species, all the other members of this group in a given area benefit from the fact that the local predators have been "educated", meaning that they have learned to recognize and stay away from insects with a particular colour pattern. It follows then that any insect displaying a pattern very much like that of the protected kind will share in the latter's immunity. After tangling a few times with a black-and-yellow hornet, or tasting an orange-and-black monarch, a bird will tend to shy away from any insect with similar coloration. This fact, proven by carefully controlled experiments, has highlighted a fascinating phenomenon: the often striking imitation, by unarmed or "edible" insects, of others that have formidable weapons, such as stings or distasteful body juices. Masquerading as protected insects, many otherwise defenceless moths, butterflies, beetles, grasshoppers, and flies manage to share in the immunity of their models. The bluff is successful, affording the imitators a much greater margin of freedom from attack than they would otherwise enjoy.

Widespread in the insect world, and creating a bewildering array of look-alikes, many of which are in no way related to one another, this particular type of masquerade is called *mimicry,* a term designating a superficial resemblance exhibited by one animal to another for purposes of protection.

Entomologists generally consider the English naturalist Henry W. Bates, a contemporary of Darwin, to be the father of the theory of mimicry. Bates spent much time collecting insects in South America. Returning home from his travels, he began to sort out his collections. Only after close inspection of the insects did he discover, to his surprise, that he had placed together certain butterflies belonging to different families, in the belief that they were members of the same species, so much did they resemble each other in shape, colouring, and wing patterns. Intrigued by this discovery, Bates pursued his studies. What he found convinced him that harmless or edible insects are benefited by imitating obnoxious or poisonous species.

Fritz Müller, a German naturalist who lived in Brazil, supplemented the theory of ''Batesian mimicry'' with a theory of his own, called Müllerian mimicry in his honour. While Bates concerned himself with the imitation, by ''edible'' insects, of protected kinds, Müller became interested in the many cases of mimicry by one protected species of another, also protected kind. Such mimicry may seem superfluous at first sight, but the fact that it serves a useful purpose becomes clear when we try to visualize how it works out in real life.

The monarch butterfly (left) and its mimic, the viceroy.

Let us assume that in a given area there are 4,000 butterflies of one inedible kind, and 8,000 of another, different-looking, but also distasteful kind. Assuming further that the birds and other insectivores of that region will destroy 1,000 butterflies before they learn to recognize one pattern, it follows that 2,000 out of a total of 12,000 butterflies must die to establish immunity for the rest. If, however, the two species resemble each other so closely that they appear the same to the predator, the losses are cut in half, and both species profit.

The above example shows that losses to both models and mimics are reduced in direct ratio to the number of species that share the same colour pattern. If five different butterflies look alike, each species will suffer roughly only one fifth of the losses it would sustain if each had a different colour pattern. And in fact, a single colour pattern does appear repeatedly in many unrelated insects living in the same area. This represents what Dr. Alexander Klots has called "modern advertising in reverse". Today's advertising, he points out, concentrates on just a few brand names, bringing them repeatedly to the attention of the prospective customer, who is finally conditioned to accept the claims of the advertisement, and to sample the product. Müllerian mimicry, with its repetition of a single warning pattern in a number of different insects, conditions the "customers"—birds, reptiles, monkeys—*not* to sample the product by reminding them of unpleasant past experiences with insect prey displaying this pattern.

We have already noted that mimicry may be so perfect as to fool even an expert. To mislead an amateur, let alone a bird, it does not have to be nearly as perfect. Most people, for example, will be extremely wary of a hornet-sized, black-and-yellow striped insect, even though it may later turn out to be a harmless moth or beetle, one of the many good wasp mimics. Several species of flies also mimic wasps, the large dangerous hornets being favoured models. One moth species looks very much like a bumblebee.

In the temperate regions, the most familiar instance of mimicry is that involving the viceroy and monarch butterflies. Although smaller than the monarch, the viceroy is a faithful mimic of its larger model's orange-and-black wing pattern. Tests have shown that the viceroy is shunned by birds that have had unpleasant experiences with monarchs, even though the viceroy belongs to a family of "edible" butterflies.

If we want to see mimicry at its best, however, we must turn to the tropics, where the struggle for survival is much fiercer than in temperate climates. Take, for example, a tropical species of

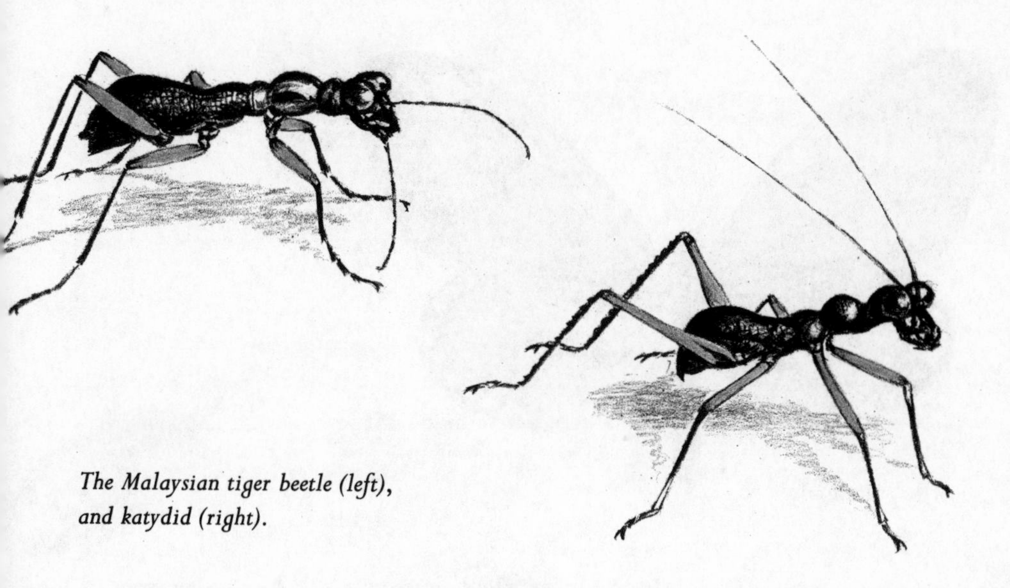

The Malaysian tiger beetle (left), and katydid (right).

katydid found in Malaysia—a harmless, plant-eating member of the grasshopper family that closely resembles a distasteful, predacious Malaysian tiger beetle. Avoided by insect-eating animals because of its obnoxious body juices, the tiger beetle walks about the jungle virtually unmolested, looking very much like a large black ant with orange legs. By mimicking this beetle, the katydid shares in its model's considerable immunity from attack. In doing so, however, it departed far from the typical shape and

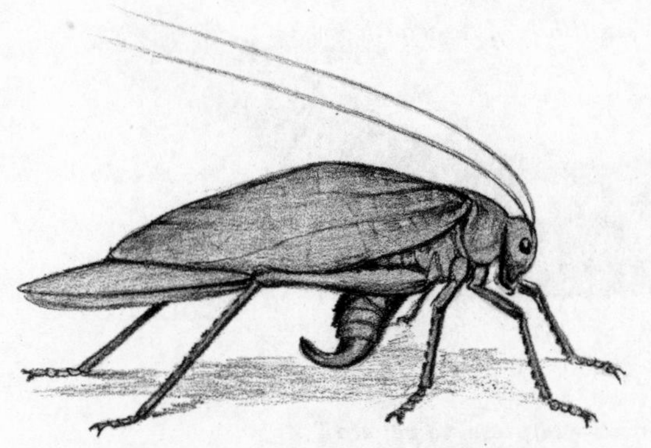

A common katydid

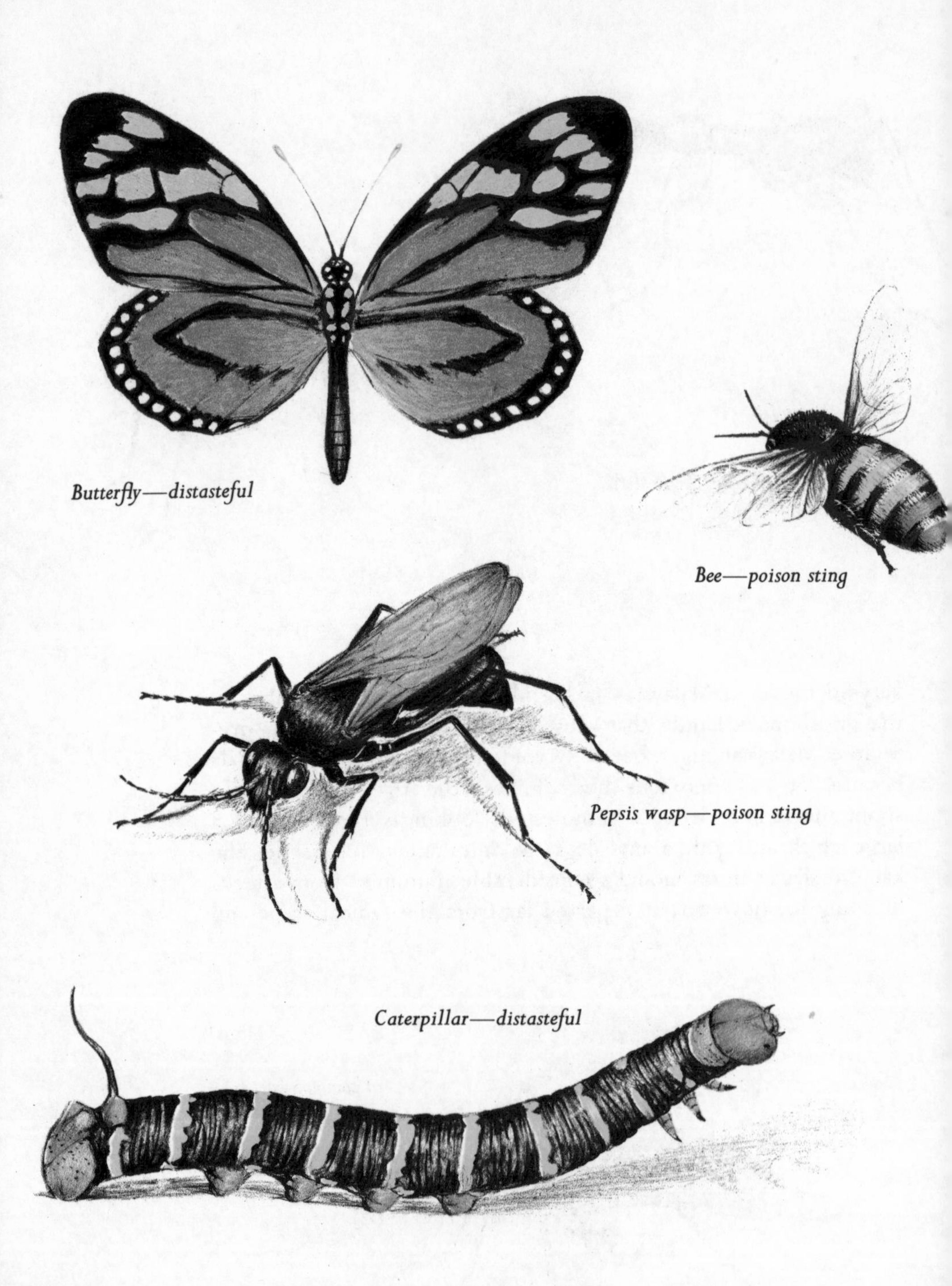

Insects with warning patterns.
All these insects have effective weapons or protective devices.

colouring of its own kind. Most katydids, whose name is derived from their familiar song, heard on summer nights and popularly interpreted as "Katy did—Katy didn't", are slender grasshoppers with green or brown wings. Their main defence is to blend in with the foliage of the trees and bushes on which they live, and to remain "planted" during the daytime much like the stick and leaf insects, becoming active only after sundown. The false Malaysian tiger beetle, black and red-legged, looks out of place in the company of its closest relatives.

While the katydid's imitation act seems astonishing enough, top prize for cradle-to-grave mimicry, covering different stages of development, undoubtedly must go to another member of the grasshopper clan—a locust that lives in Borneo. Locusts are short-horned grasshoppers, meaning that they have short antennae. In many parts of the world, these insects periodically appear in huge swarms that destroy all vegetation wherever they settle to feed. (The so-called seventeen-year locust of North America is not a grasshopper but a cicada which was misnamed by settlers from Europe)

The Malaysian locust is a perfectionist, mimicking not one, but *three* different species of tiger beetles! To appreciate fully this example of mimicry one must keep in mind that the development of a locust and a beetle is fundamentally different. The beetle, which has complex metamorphosis, emerges from the pupa a fully grown adult and remains the same size for the rest of its life. A locust, on the other hand, has a gradual metamorphosis and spends much of its time as a nymph. For a fully grown locust to mimic a tiger beetle of the same size, it must first pass safely through the smaller larval stages when it is especially vulnerable to attack by predators. The locust from Borneo has solved this problem very neatly by mimicking three different tiger-beetle species of different

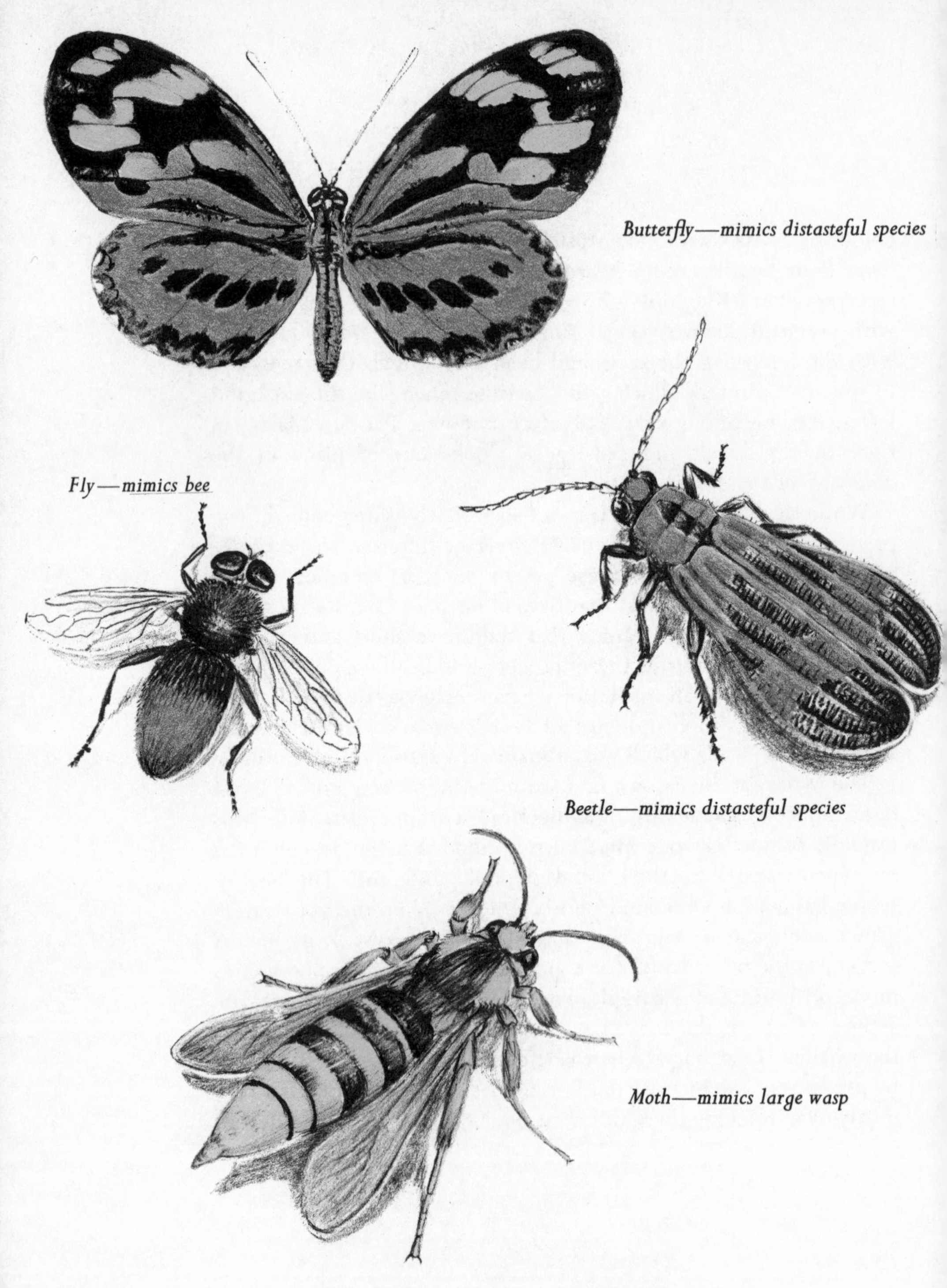

Insects that mimic, by their colouring and patterns, other insects which are genuinely protected. None of the mimics is dangerous or distasteful.

sizes: a small one when the locust is very young, a medium-sized one when it is half-grown, and a large beetle when it is fully grown and mature.

How this three-act masquerade came to be discovered is an interesting story. The first specimens of this locust to be recognized as such were not identified in the field; instead, a museum collection was found to contain the insect in various stages of development, classified as different species of tiger beetles! Thus even the experts had been fooled by the locust's unusually good mimicry.

In some cases, especially among butterflies, mimicry is confined to one sex only. Throughout the animal world, we find instances of what is called *sexual dimorphism,* meaning a difference in appearance between the male and female of a species. Among birds especially, the male is often very brilliantly coloured, while the female has duller, subtler colours. This protective colouring gives her an advantage during the time she has to care for her eggs and young, by making it more difficult for predators to spot her.

Among insects in which sexual dimorphism occurs because of mimicry, the roles are reversed. Here it is the female that is more conspicuous, because she mimics the bright, bold colour patterns of a model advertising its inedibility.

One of the best known of these cases involves a member of the milkweed-butterfly family, to which the monarch also belongs. This butterfly, distasteful like all the other members of its group, is mimicked by the females only of two entirely different species of edible butterflies, the African swallowtail *Papilio dardanus* and *Hypolimnas misippus,* a member of the world-wide nymphalid family, which includes such butterflies as the painted lady and the rare Camberwell beauty.

The African swallowtail normally has dark wings with large

white areas, and its hind wings usually have the "tails" that are so typical of its kind. In some parts of Africa, however, the females of the species have not only lost the tails but have changed their colouring and wing pattern so that they closely resemble the orange-brown, white, and black wing colours of *Danaüs chrysippus,* the golden danaïd of Africa and Asia.

The male of *Hypolimnas misippus* also retains the ancestral colouring of its kind, black with a large bluish-white spot on the forewings,

The Male of Papilio dardanus *displays the ancestral shape and colouring of its kind.*

◀ *The golden danaïd (top) is mimicked by females of* Hypolimnas misippus *(centre) and* Papilio dardanus *(bottom).*

while the female has adopted the predominantly orange-brown colouring of the distasteful danaïd.

The result is that we have three different species in which the females look very much alike, though they belong to three entirely different families, while the males of two of the three do not look as if they were related to the females of their own kind.

If that sounds somewhat confusing, it is nothing compared to the confusion created by mimicry in the tropics of the New World. Highly distasteful models, most of which belong to several groups of monarch relatives, and many of which mimic each other, are found in the company of edible mimics coming from a variety of butterfly families. What with all this Batesian and Müllerian mimicry and sexual dimorphism, it is no wonder that most predators learn to leave the entire group alone. All we have to do is to put ourselves in the position of a bird or monkey unlucky enough to get hold of one of these distasteful butterflies several times in a row. After that, any insect displaying a similar colour pattern is likely to be exempt from attack by this predator. Because of the marvellous freedom which they enjoy, these families of monarch relatives, among which Müllerian mimicry is so widespread, are considered by entomologists to be the most advanced group of the entire Lepidoptera order.

When we look at the many different protected insects which "advertise" their individual defensive devices by warning coloration, the thing that strikes us is the prevalence of the so-called warm colours—yellow, orange, red—in these patterns. This brings to mind the fact that we humans also use these colours for symbols that caution or warn of danger—the red stop light, the red flags at construction sites, the yellow Belisha beacons, orange paint on aeroplanes, and the yellow helmets, raincoats, and other clothing for people working at danger spots. Colours from the "warm" side of the visible spectrum are chosen to get fastest attention. The reason is that the human eye sees—or rather, the brain registers—a warm colour more quickly than a cool colour, such as blue. It is probably not a coincidence that so many distasteful insects display a lot of red, orange, and yellow, for there is evidence that the colour vision of birds and reptiles is not so very different from that of humans, whereas the majority of mammals, man's closest relatives in the animal kingdom, seem to be more or less colour-blind.

Even though not much is known about the evolution of mimicry, it is easy for us to understand its purpose as well as its usefulness to those insects that practise it in their struggle for existence. In contrast, the peculiar but seemingly senseless "costumes" worn by the insects we shall meet in the next chapter present an intriguing and fascinating puzzle.

The day-flying syntomid moth has warning coloration.

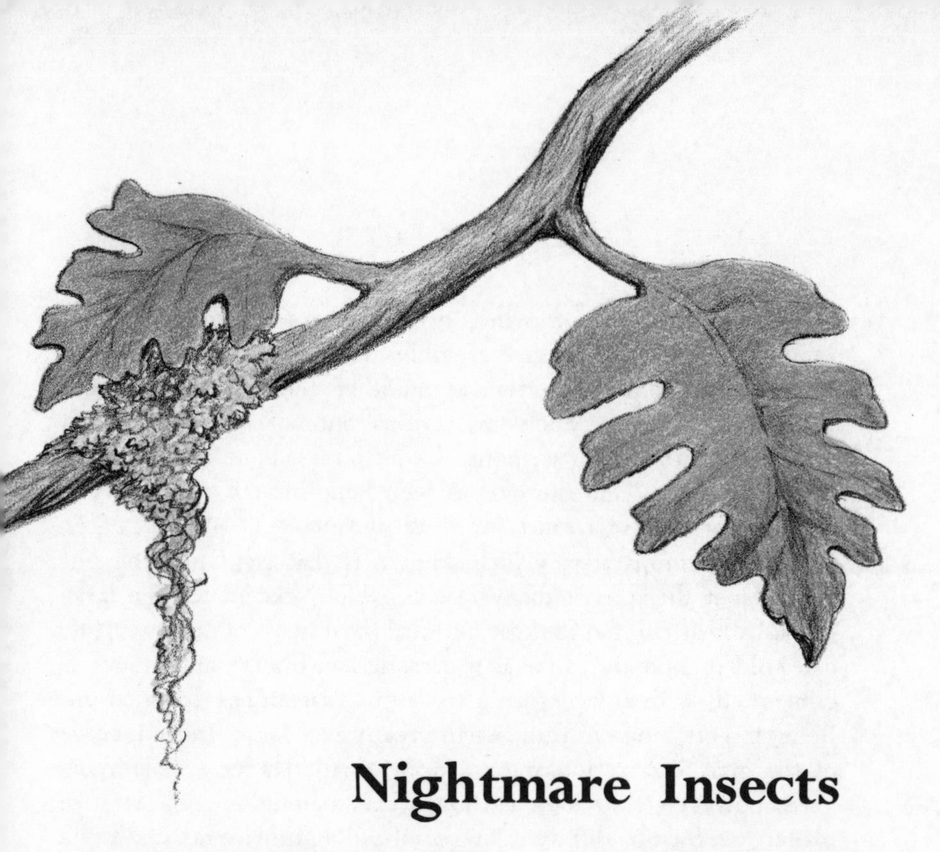

Nightmare Insects

HAVE YOU EVER SEEN an insect from outer space? If you happen to be an avid reader of science-fiction stories, chances are that you have seen an imaginary one—on the cover of a story dealing with life on other planets. Fear-inspiring creatures that invade our earth from some other world have long been a prominent feature of science-fiction writing. Now, however, with the possibility of a flight to the moon—or even to Mars—fast becoming a reality, many of these stories deal with the life found by us as *we* invade other planets.

All the same, at the present time nobody knows whether life on other planets does indeed exist, and much less what it may look like. The imagination of science-fiction writers, unfettered by facts, is free to dream up any creature it pleases. They can—and do—picture inhabitants of other worlds in shapes ranging from mechanical robots to moving, breathing, intelligent vegetables. Inevitably, some of them resemble insects, usually large, and invested with additional antennae and other appendages sticking out from their bodies. Such mysterious antennae are frequently associated with "superweapons"—death rays, bone-melting high-frequency waves, and the like. A weird and bizarre appearance is in any case almost a must for these imaginary creatures.

What is comparatively little known is that right here on our own planet there exist many insects which, except for the large size usually attributed to these fictional inhabitants of other worlds, can hold their own, as far as grotesque and bizarre appearance is concerned, with anything an artist's imagination has dreamed up. Being insects, none of these earth creatures is large. Indeed, some of the most bizarre-looking are quite small. Under a magnifying glass, however, they look as though they belong on some strange planet governed by different laws of life. "Nightmare insects", one naturalist has called them, and this is an apt description for many of them.

There is a story, told around the turn of the century, of a man fighting his way through the jungles of the Amazon in search of

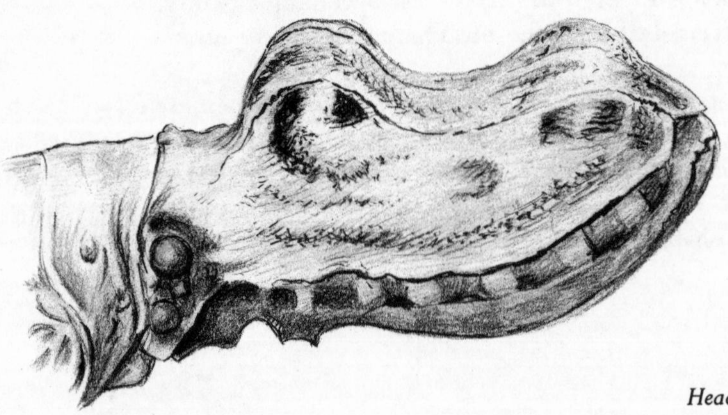

Head of the alligator bug,
showing the fake crocodile's face on the snout.
Real eyes are at lower left.

rubber trees. Seventy years ago, such an expedition was a much riskier undertaking than it would be nowadays. Lost in the swamp-infested forests, the man fell ill, and in his fever dreams was plagued by visions of huge insects with heads like alligators descending upon him. Swarming about, they came in for the attack, their sharp teeth ready to tear him to pieces. Most of this story—especially the large size and aggressive nature of these insects—was a product of the man's fever. The insects themselves, however, were real enough.

There is in the jungles of Brazil a strange bug with a wingspread of about six inches. (The word "bug" is used here, not incorrectly as a synonym for "insect," but to designate a member of the large insect order called Homoptera). The anterior portion of this insect's head is the size of a large peanut, seemingly much too heavy to be carried around by its owner, for it measures one third of the entire body length. Appearances are deceiving in this case, for the structure is largely hollow and very light. Its most amazing feature, however, is the way the light and dark markings on the bug's snout combine to create the illusion of a crocodilian face—eyes, nostrils, teeth, and all. The real eyes of the insect are small, located behind and below the staring false ones. Although it is a perfectly harmless, plant-eating creature, one good look at the grinning reptilian face makes it easy to understand how it could loom large as a fierce and dangerous predator in a sick man's feverish nightmares. This strange insect is called a lantern fly, a very misleading name because it is not a fly, nor does it give off light, despite persistent stories to the contrary. Its other popular name, alligator bug, is much more descriptive and more accurate.

The lantern fly provides an excellent example of overdevelopment of one part of the body, which grows out of all proportion, often

The Chinese candle fly is often said to be luminous, but no evidence has been found to support this belief.

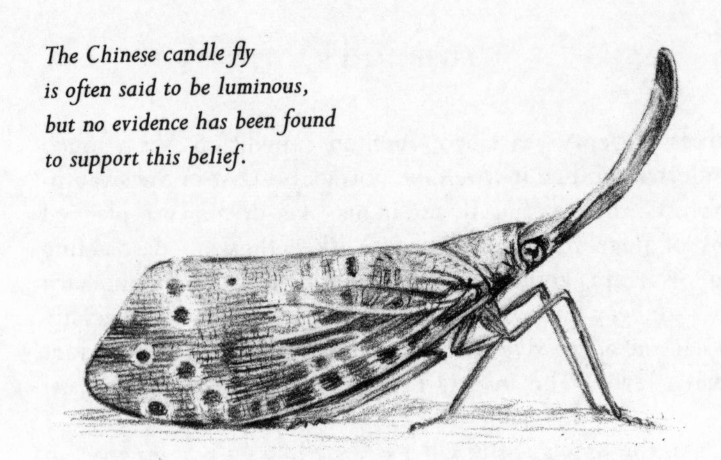

assuming peculiar shapes. Known as hypertrophy—literally, excessive growth—this phenomenon is found in a variety of insects, affecting different parts of the body—head thorax, wing cases, legs—in different species.

In the case of the lantern fly and its close relative, the Chinese candle fly, only the snout has suffered hypertrophic growth, but in other species, the entire head may be long and narrow, or else thinned out so that it protrudes at both sides of the body, forming long horizontal stalks. This kind of hypertrophic growth is displayed by a small group of mostly tropical flies, and creates a most outlandish appearance, especially in the more extreme forms. Since the eyes are located at the very tips of these stalks, in some species each eye may be more than a body length removed from the centre of the head! For comparison, imagine, if you can, that your eyes were located at the tips of poles sticking out five or six feet to the right and left of your head, like horizontal periscopes, and you will be ready to sympathize with the stalk-eyed flies. For one thing, walking around would prove most awkward, especially since vision up front would be practically nil.

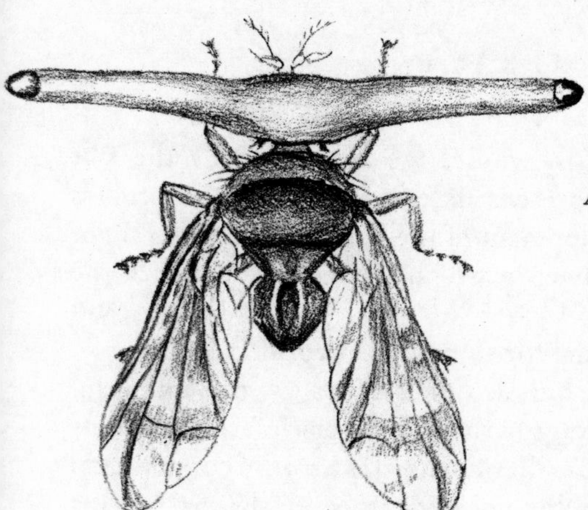

A species of stalk-eyed fly with oversized head and tiny body.

Although the flies obviously do not need our sympathy, as they seem to be able to hold their own and survive, nobody would deny that the eye stalks, far from having any useful function, must hamper the insect's freedom of movement. They are not retractable like the eye stalks of a snail, which not only serve a purpose, but also grow from an otherwise normally shaped head. In the case of the stalk-eyed fly, whose head is extended like a piece of rubber that has been pulled from both ends to make it long and thin, the tiny feelers have, in some instances, moved right along with the eyes to the tips of the stalks.

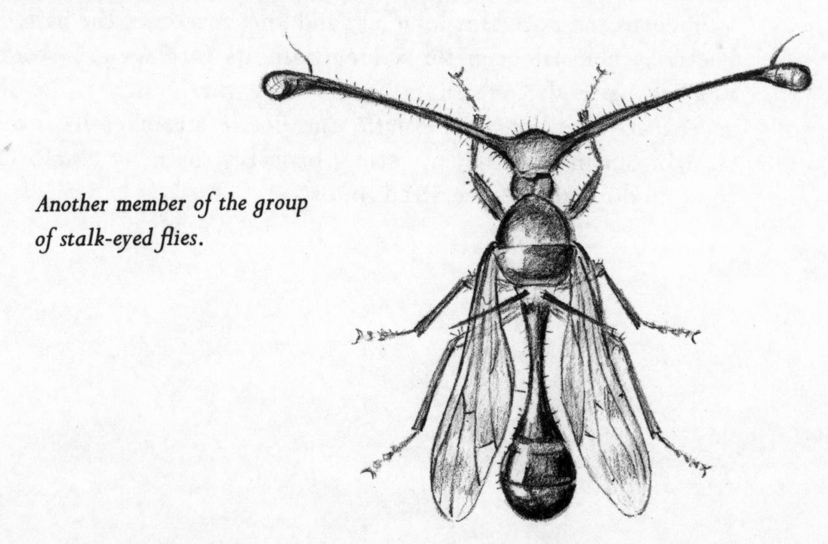

Another member of the group of stalk-eyed flies.

Looking at the group as a whole, we are struck by the fact that the various species represent different stages in the process of the horizontal over-development of the head—from just a slight broadening to an extreme one, in which the distance between the eyes measures several times the body length. Enlarge this fly, and you will have a perfect model for some other-world creature.

Not just the head alone, but also its appendages, the antennae, are subject to hypertrophic growth. The antennae are extremely important to an insect because they function as a sort of combination nose and fingers, and possibly in some species also as hearing organs. Their shape and size vary according to the species' individual needs. Accordingly, they may be short or long, thin or broad, feathery or comb-like, knobbed or tapering. It is difficult to see, however, what any insect would want with antennae that are four times as long as its body! Yet there is a beetle equipped with such oversized feelers, and nobody has yet been able to suggest a valid reason for their extensive length.

Long legs, so necessary to the modern fashion model, are also an outstanding feature of many insects, but for different reasons. Adapted for running or jumping, they do come in handy when a fast getaway has to be made and flying is not feasible. But even good things can be overdone, and that seems to have happened in the case of a beetle found in the forests of Brazil, and other parts of South America. One of the longhorn beetles, a group also called longicorns and noted for long legs and long antennae, the harlequin beetle is unusual even for a longhorn. Its forelegs are twice as long as its body, which measures over three inches. As if to accentuate their unusual length, the beetle stretches its forelegs straight out in front when resting, probably the most comfortable thing to do with the oversized limbs.

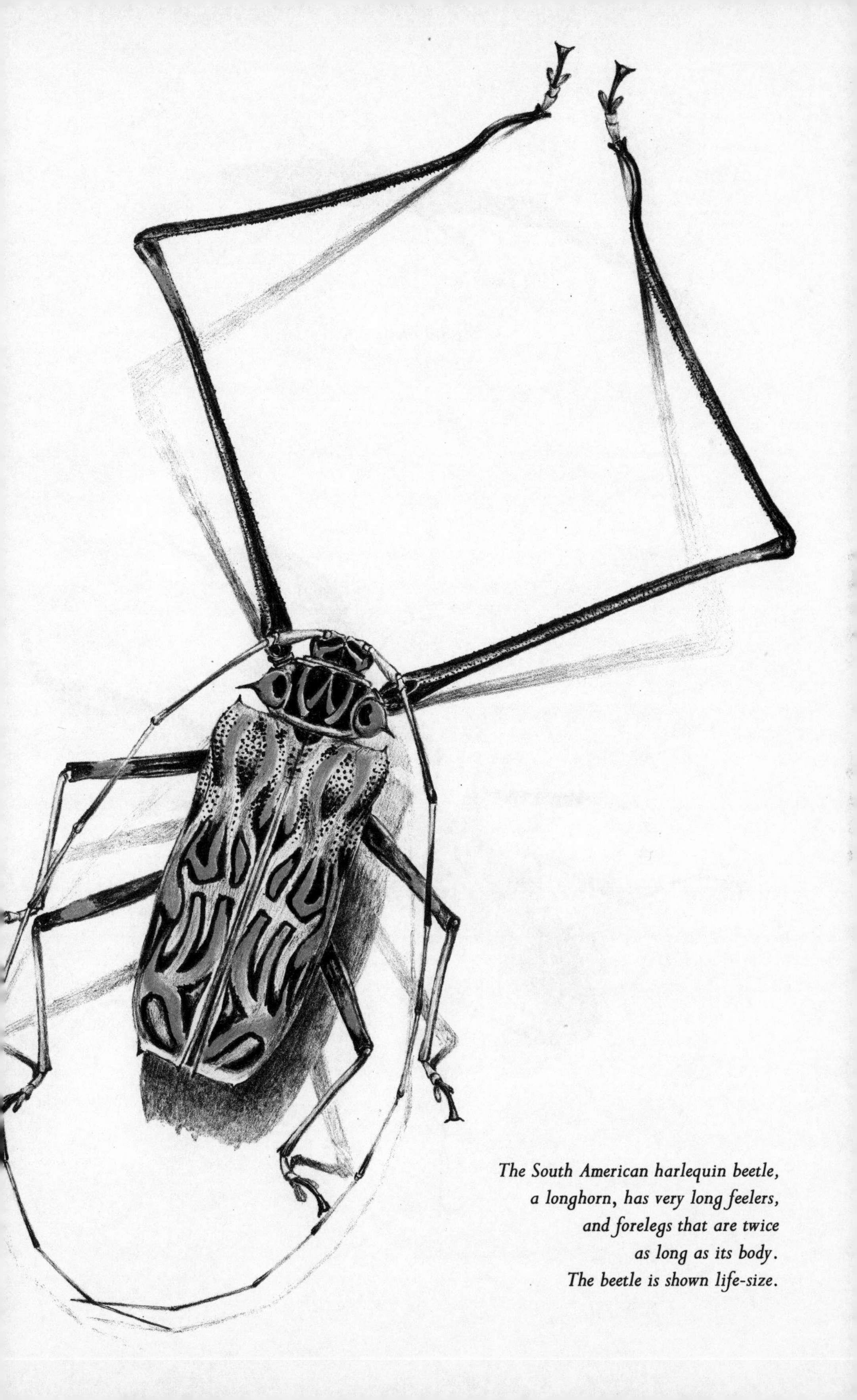

*The South American harlequin beetle,
a longhorn, has very long feelers,
and forelegs that are twice
as long as its body.
The beetle is shown life-size.*

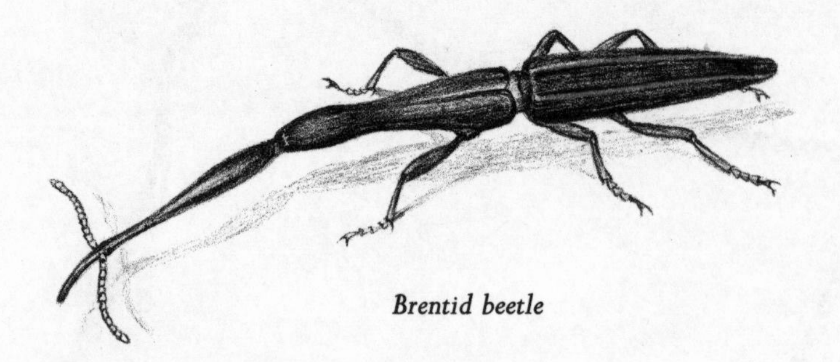

Brentid beetle

Stag beetle

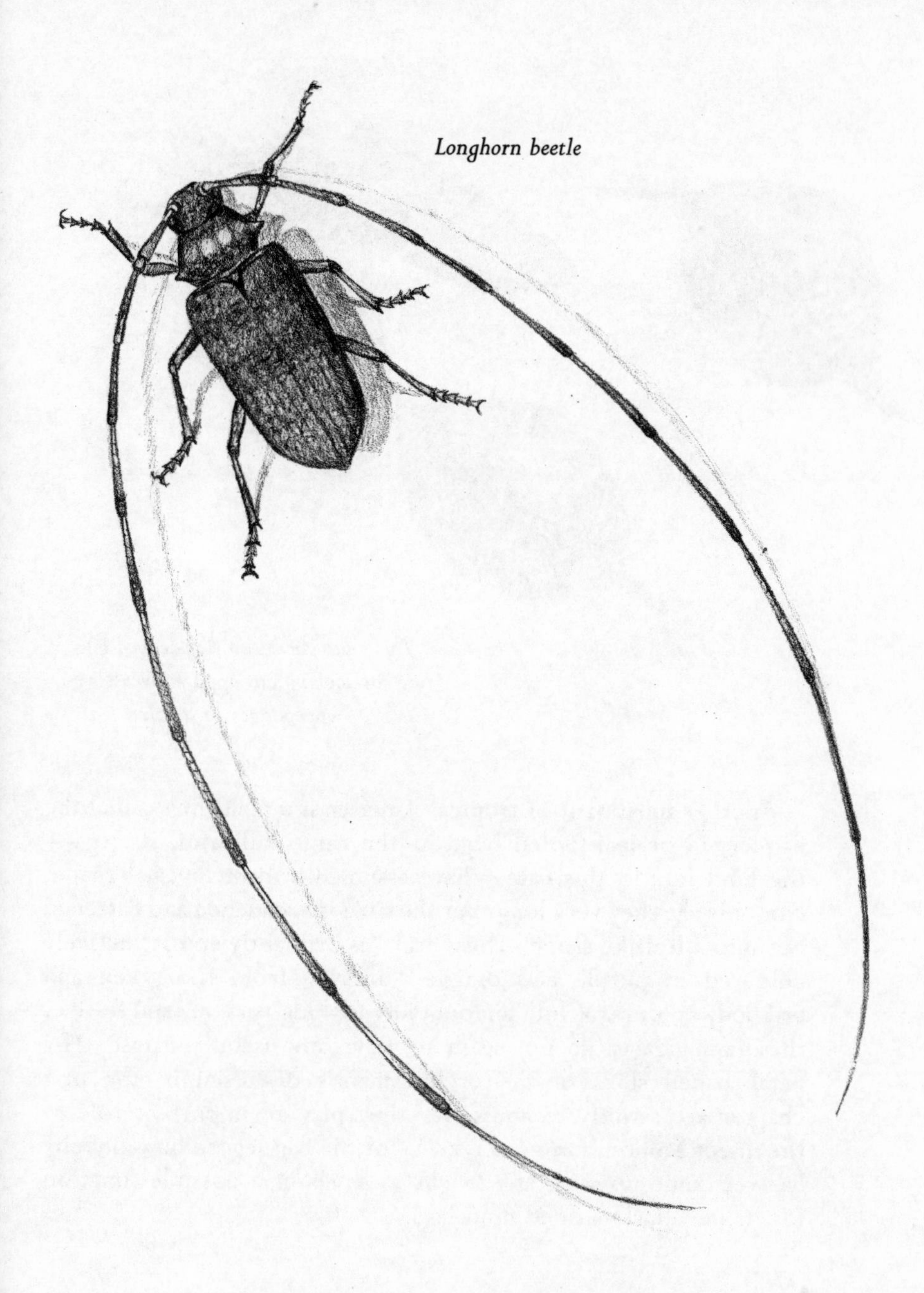

Three beetles with different kinds of hypertrophic growth.

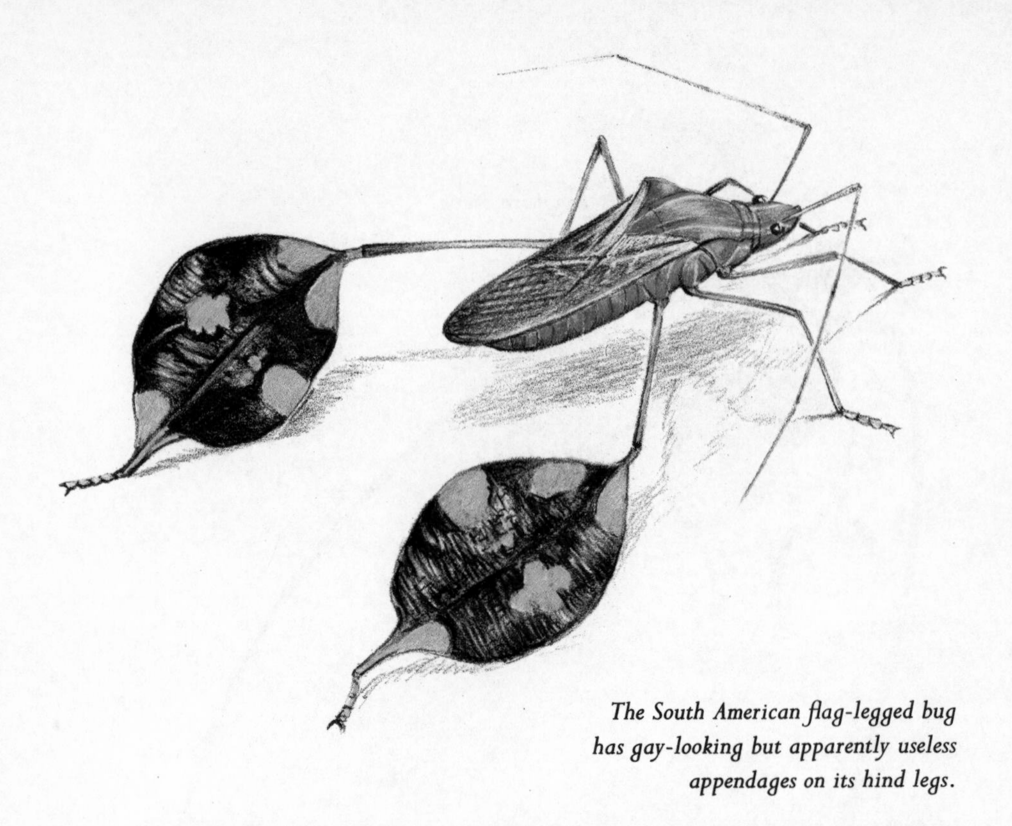

The South American flag-legged bug has gay-looking but apparently useless appendages on its hind legs.

Another inhabitant of tropical America is a plant bug called the flag-legged or leaf-footed bug. As the name indicates, its legs—the hind legs in this case—have assumed a most unusual shape. Not only are they very long, but the tibia is broadened and flattened out into a leaflike shape. This "leaf" is brilliantly and attractively coloured in purple and orange, differing from the green and red body colours. While undoubtedly looking very gay and festive, these appendages do not seem to serve any useful purpose. The petal-shaped shins of the orchid mantis discussed in the first chapter are strictly business, for they play an important role in the insect's ambush camouflage. As for the flag-legged bug, nobody has yet come up with any bright ideas about a possible function for its peculiarly-shaped hind legs.

Though little known to the general public, insects with body oddities, especially the larger-sized ones, have long been favourites of insect collectors. Occasionally huge sums have been paid for specimens considered rare, as in the case of a peculiar beetle found in the Indo-Australian region. Called the fiddler because of its shape, the beetle does somewhat resemble a violin. While its wing covers, the elytra, are enormously drawn out and flattened, its head and thorax are long and thin. Although this insect subsequently was found to be fairly common, a French museum reportedly paid 4,000 francs for a single specimen at a time when it was still considered a rarity!

With all the strange shapes and growths we have reviewed thus far, we have not even touched upon the most peculiar of them all, leaving the best—in this case, the most grotesque—for the last. In the entire insect class, there is no other single group with so many bizarre-looking members as the family of tree hoppers, which are relatives of the cicadas. Tree hoppers are mostly small insects which rarely exceed half an inch in length, and most of them are

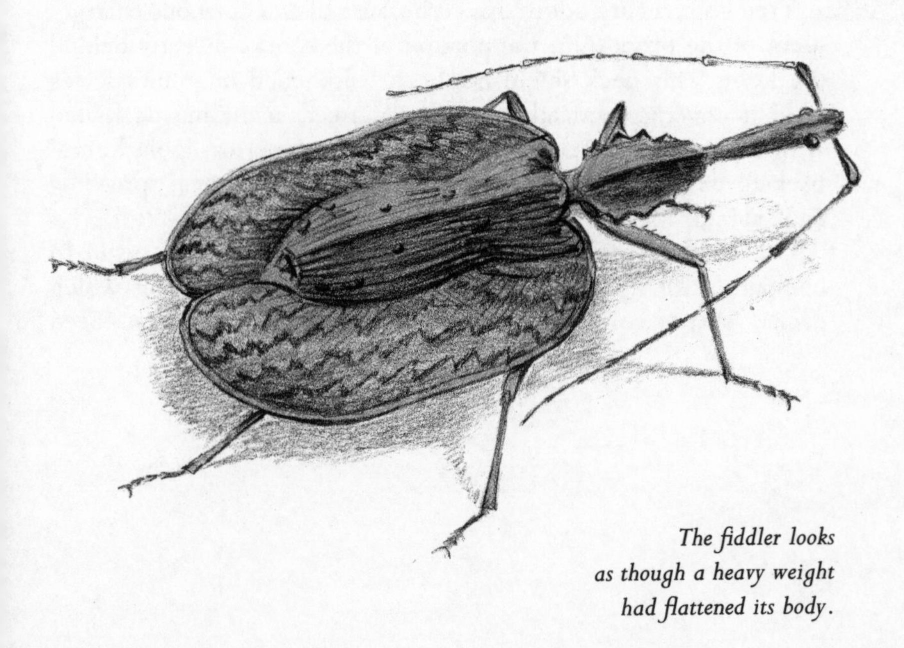

The fiddler looks as though a heavy weight had flattened its body.

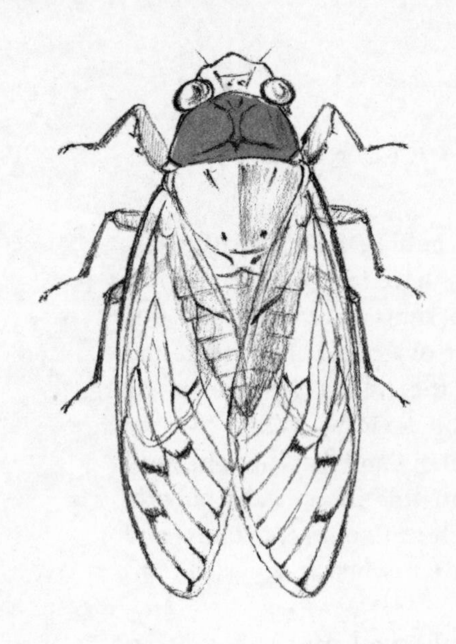

Diagram of a cicada.
The pronotum, the portion of the thorax which is greatly enlarged in the related tree hoppers, is shown in red.

little more than a quarter of an inch long. They live on a variety of plants, feeding on their juices, and jump around vigorously if they are disturbed. Most members of the family, including the two hundred species found in North America, are coloured brown or green, but some tropical species have red, orange, and yellow colouring, which highlights their grotesque appearance.

Tree hoppers are oddly shaped because of an enormous enlargement of the pronotum, the portion of the thorax directly behind the head. This neck shield has been lengthened in some species until it covers practically the entire insect, including its folded wings. The buffalo tree hopper, common in America, looks humpbacked, its head and body barely visible under its huge, spreading neck shield.

Odd as this tree hopper may appear, it cannot even begin to compete with its relatives south of the border, some of which display shapes so grotesque that they beggar description. Seen

The buffalo tree hopper,
a common American species.

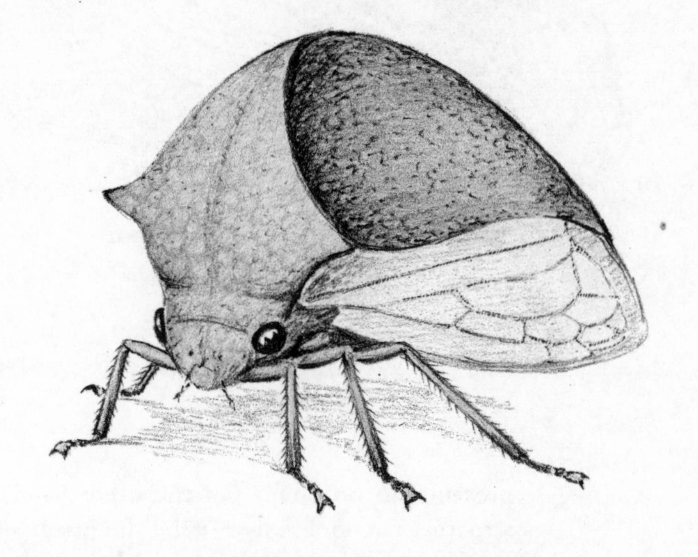

under a magnifying glass, so that each detail stands out, many of these creatures look like the product of some surrealist artist's lighter moments. One, for example, carries on its neck a crescent-shaped structure rising to several times the height of the insect. Another one has a superstructure that grows from a helmet-shaped neck shield high above the head, branching out in five symmetrically arranged arms tipped with little balls, while a sixth arm, long and needle-like, extends backwards the entire length of the insect. The over-all effect is that of a minature candelabra balanced on the head of the hopper.

Even with the most graphic description, these structures have to be seen to be believed. We find crescents, sails, balls, horns, spikes, and a variety of other shapes—each more grotesque than the last—most of them completely dwarfing the insect beneath. Some of them look much too big and heavy to be carried around by their small owners, but they are actually very light, so weight

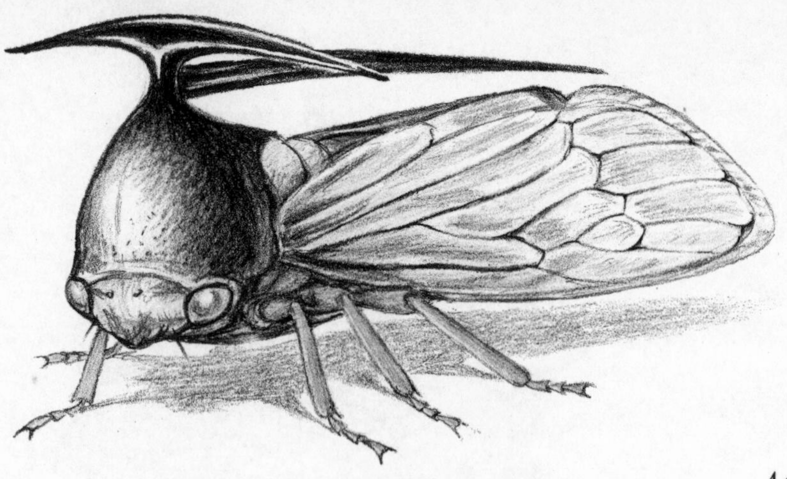

A tree hopper with a peculiar three-pronged helmet.

presents no problem. On the other hand, many of these superstructures undoubtedly restrict the insect's freedom of movement, so that they necessarily must prove to be a nuisance. To those enthusiasts of the evolutionary theory who insist that each and every form found in nature must have a function, the tree hoppers present a sticky problem. Admittedly, some of the thorn-shaped growths, which all but hide the insect's body, are useful as camouflage. When these hoppers rest quietly on a thorny twig, they are virtually invisible, and almost certain to be overlooked by birds and other insectivores. For the majority, however, there is no such advantage, as is obvious from the examples described earlier.

Although there have been many attempts to find an answer to the apparently inexplicable—to assign some function to these peculiar hypertrophic growths—these efforts have not been successful. Today most biologists content themselves with the statement that such bizarre shapes represent instances of evolution run wild and off the tracks. Some naturalists, however, point out that we have finally come to realize that all decisive changes in living organisms are the result of unknown forces working within the genes. The fact that some of them later turn out to be functional, and others not, cannot be interpreted to mean that only the forms that we consider functional "make sense".

In view of such arguments, it seems advisable to keep an open mind, and not simply dismiss something as senseless just because we do not understand it at the present time. We must not forget how often new scientific discoveries render obsolete a scientific theory or opinion that has been long accepted and believed. In the same way, future research in the field of biology may force us to reappraise or even discard many of our present ideas.

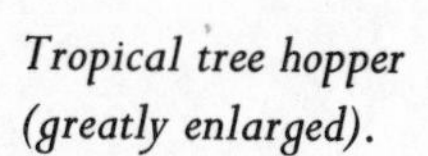

Tropical tree hopper (greatly enlarged).

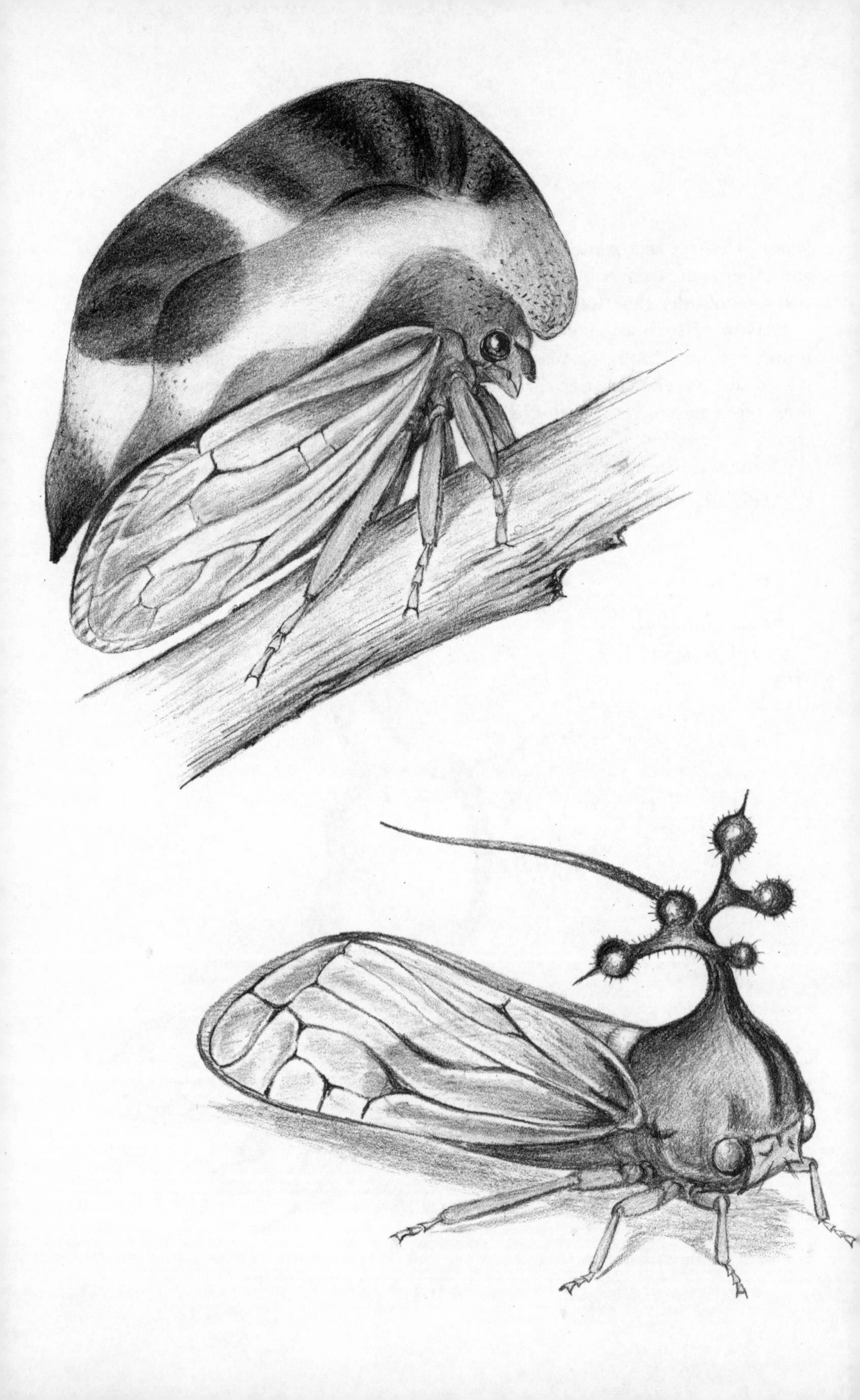

These three species of tropical tree hoppers represent some of the most bizarre forms of hypertrophic growth found in the insect world.

In the meantime, in a world increasingly oriented towards the exploration of outer space, our "nightmare insects" can help remind us of the fact that mysteries abound right here on earth. Such little creatures invite us to seek greater knowledge and understanding, with humility in the realization of how little we know about the forces of life even as expressed in its humbler forms.

A Guide to Finding Masqueraders in the Garden

Reading about the fascinating insects described in this book and even seeing their pictures cannot compare to the fun of searching them out and observing them in their natural surroundings.

Of course, the average person can hardly hope to see some of the exotic species shown here, except, perhaps, as mounted specimens in a museum. Few people outside of naturalists travelling in the tropics would have the opportunity to observe live specimens of such strange creatures as the orchid mantis or the alligator bug. Nor would they be able to sort out fact from fiction in the frequently colourful local stories told about these insects. One American entomologist was presented with an alligator bug which reportedly had just killed a man. So far, however, no evidence of a capacity to inflict a fatal bite has been found by naturalists collecting these bugs.

But even though the temperate zones may not be able to boast of such exotic and exciting mystery creatures, some of the insects—or closely related species—described in this book may be found in gardens, woods and meadows, or on a beach nearby. Frank E. Lutz, a noted entomologist who was formerly the head of the insect department of the American Museum of Natural History in New York, once said that he believed he could find about a thousand different kinds of insects in the average back garden. This was doubted by one of his colleagues, who remarked that a thousand was "a lot of insects" for so small an area. Dr. Lutz took up the challenge, set about looking for insects in a garden—and found, not a thousand, but close to fifteen hundred different species! He published the results of this search in book form. The title? *A Lot of Insects*.

It is not suggested that the interested reader of this book should attempt to match Mr. Lutz's performance. But with a little patience, you should not have much difficulty in locating, during the course of a summer, most of the insects listed below.

DOODLEBUGS Ant lions are common in Southern Europe and you may come across them on continental holidays. The larvae usually dig their pits in sandy or other loose soil, under rocky ledges or near houses. Various species of tiger beetles can be found in many parts of Britain. They live on sandy heaths and among sand-dunes. Their larvae dig their burrows in the sand. It takes a somewhat trained eye to spot the head of a doodlebug plugging the entrance hole.

BARK AND LEAF MOTHS Most gardens will yield a large number of moth species—many of them more or less serious plant pests—which have green or brown cryptic colouring that camouflages them when sitting on a tree or among foliage. Some bark moths may be attracted at night by smearing tree trunks with a mixture of sugar and fermented fruit juice. The large hawk moths sit quietly during the day among foliage or on trees, but fly when dusk falls; they visit tubular flowers such as petunias, honeysuckle, and trumpet vine, whose nectar they can reach with their long sucking tubes.

LOOPERS Many species of these caterpillars, both green and brown kinds, can be found in any garden. Some are extremely hard to detect because of their excellent imitation of small twigs.

WATER STICK INSECT In some ponds in the south, there is a long water-bug, which because it looks rather like the real stick insects is often called the water stick insect, but its real name is the long water-scorpion. It sits quietly on the bottom of the pond and is not easy to see. When its prey comes within reach it quickly secures it with its long front legs.

WASP-MIMICKING MOTHS A number of clearwing moths are excellent wasp mimics. One species mimics a large hornet. The best way to tell black-and-yellow wasp mimics, which may be moths, flies, or beetles, from the real wasps is by acquainting yourself with the distinguishing characteristics of wasps and hornets.

GRASSHOPPERS Many species of grasshoppers and crickets, relations of the katydids, occur in various parts of the country, among grass. They are either brown or green in colour and often very hard to see until they leap or sing.

MONARCH The monarch, or milkweed butterfly, occasionally finds its way to Britain, so keep a look out for it. A large number were seen in 1968. Unfortunately, the milkweed plants on which its caterpillars feed do not grow here, and so it can never establish itself in Britain.

LONGHORNS Although they are not as spectacular as the tropical harlequin beetle, many longhorns found in temperate regions are distinguished by oversize antennae. The timberman, whose larva digs galleries under the bark of fallen pine trees, has feelers that are four times as long as its body. It lives in Scotland.

PATTERNS OF INSECT DEVELOPMENT

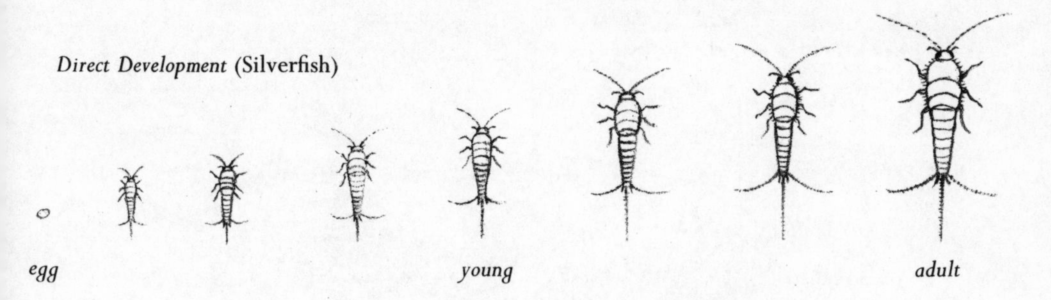

The most primitive insects have a *direct* development (no metamorphosis), in which the young resemble the adults in all details.

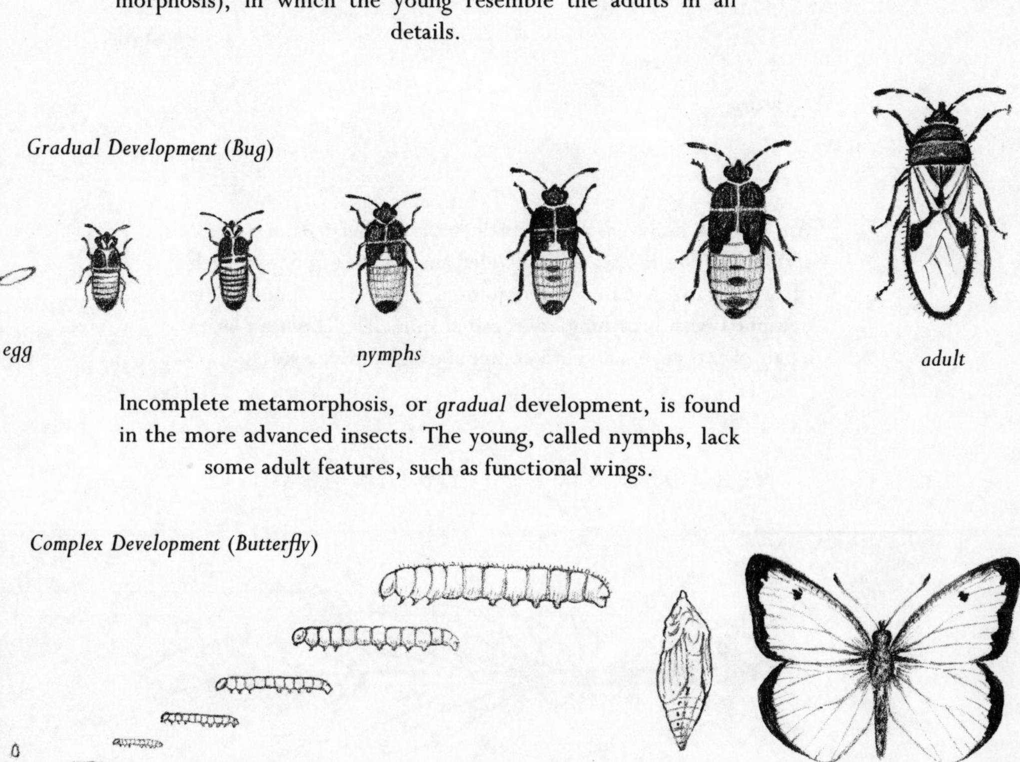

Incomplete metamorphosis, or *gradual* development, is found in the more advanced insects. The young, called nymphs, lack some adult features, such as functional wings.

The most advanced insects go through a *complex* development (complete metamorphosis), which involves four stages: egg, larva, pupa, and adult. The immature insect does not resemble the adult.

PARTS OF AN INSECT'S BODY

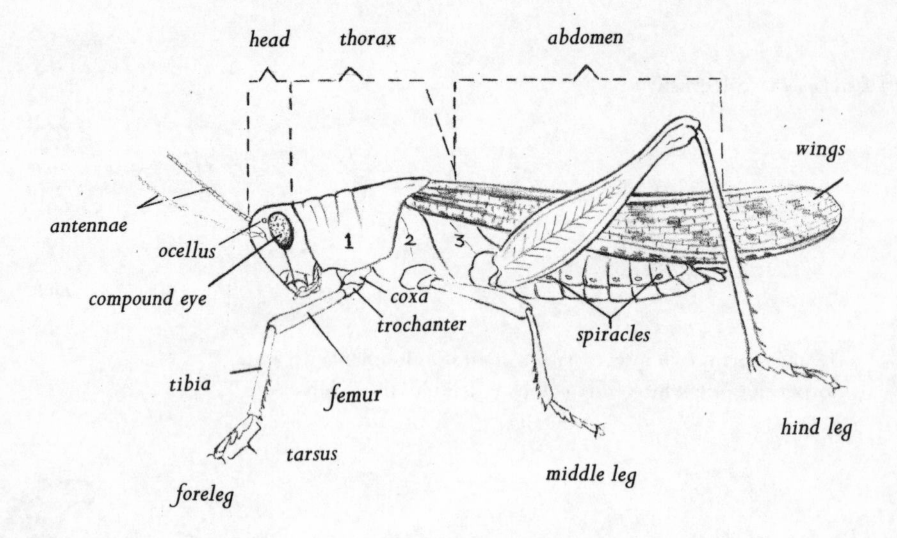

An insect's body has three distinct parts: head, thorax, and abdomen. The thorax is subdivided into three segments, each of which has a pair of five-jointed legs. The abdomen is equipped with breathing holes called spiracles. The head bears a pair of antennae, and both compound and simple eyes.

NERVOUS SYSTEM OF AN INSECT

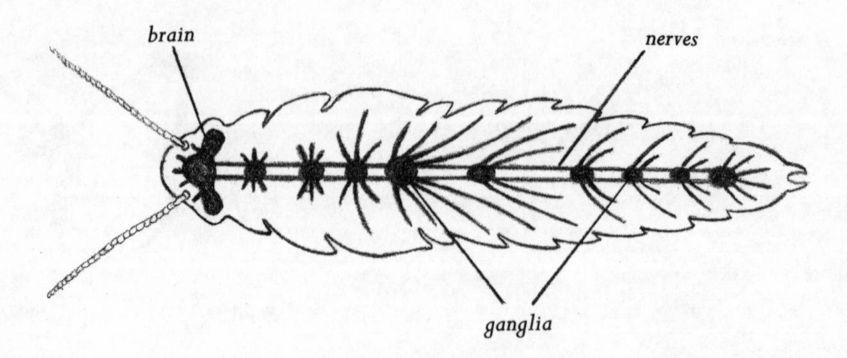

The insect brain is small and does not control the entire body. Additional nerve centres, called *ganglia* (singular: *ganglion*), serve as auxiliary "brains".

Suggestions for Further Reading

Burton, John. *The Oxford Book of Insects*. Oxford University Press, 1968.

Clegg, John. *Insects*. Muller, 1969.

Imms, A. D. *Insect Natural History*. Collins, 1947.

Linssen, E. F. & Newman, L. H. *The Observer's Book of Common Insects & Spiders*. Warne, 1964.

Newman, L. H. *Instructions to Young Naturalists: Insects*. Museum Press, 1958.

Oldroyd, H. *Insects and their World*. British Museum (Natural History), 1960.

Riley, N. D. (Editor). *Insects in Colour*. Blandford Press, 1963.

Urquhart, F. A. *Introducing the Insect*. Warne, 1965.

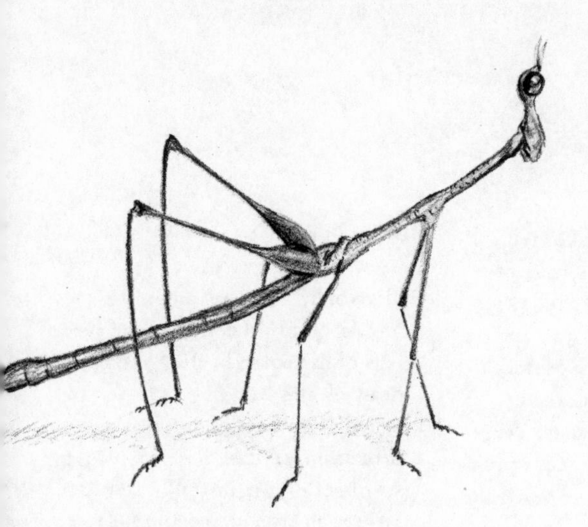

Index